THE BEST OF TEACHER'S HELPER® Magazine

Literature

GRADES 2–3

Spark students' interest in literature with this timesaving collection of reproducibles and activities. *The Best of* Teacher's Helper® *Literature* features skill-based activities tied to quality children's literature. These activities were selected from issues of *The* Grades 2–3 *Teacher's Helper®* magazine, published between 1991 and 1997. Each teacher-created unit includes the following:

- Skill-based reproducibles
- Background for the teacher
- Author information
- Cross-curricular or hands-on extensions

*** Note to the teacher:** All of the books featured in this fabulous resource were in print at the time the original magazine units were published. We've taken care to choose featured units and books for this resource that are currently in print, but cannot guarantee that every book featured will remain in print. Should you have trouble locating any of the titles featured herein, check with your media specialist.*

Editor:
Kim T. Griswell

Artists:
Jennifer Tipton Bennett, Cathy Spangler Bruce, Pam Crane, Teresa Davidson, Nick Greenwood, Clevell Harris, Susan Hodnett, Sheila Krill, Rob Mayworth, Kimberly Richard, Rebecca Saunders, Barry Slate, Donna K. Teal

Cover Artist:
Jennifer Tipton Bennett

©1999 by THE EDUCATION CENTER, INC.
All rights reserved.
ISBN #1-56234-271-1

D1127776

Manufactured in the United States
10 9 8 7 6 5 4 3 2 1

Table Of Contents

Name _____

Arthur's Study Game

Arthur needs your help to study his spelling words.
Read each word meaning.
Write the word on the line.
Use the Word Bank.

to move straight ahead	the day after today

 a contest to find the best speller

 a prize given to the winner

 a place where sea animals are kept

 a kind of candy

 the class before first grade

 spoke softly

 the person in charge of an elementary school

Word Bank

spellathon	whispered
kindergarten	aquarium
forward	trophy
principal	chocolate
tomorrow	finally

 at last

Bonus Box: Make your own set of flash cards to help you study! Write your spelling words on 3" x 5" cards. Practice with a friend.

Extension Activities

Task Cards

— Duplicate the following task card patterns onto tagboard and program in the following ways:
  — with comprehension questions from any of the Arthur books
  — with vocabulary words
  — with story starters for creative writing about Arthur

— Before duplicating, enlarge the task card patterns and add numbered lines. Duplicate and use for spelling sheets.

Task Card Patterns

©The Education Center, Inc. • *The Best Of* Teacher's Helper® *Literature* • *Grades 2–3* • TEC1473

©The Education Center, Inc. • *The Best Of* Teacher's Helper® *Literature* • *Grades 2–3* • TEC1473

Answer Key

forward	tomorrow	spellathon
trophy	aquarium	chocolate
kindergarten	whispered	principal
		finally

Name _____

Arthur's Character Code

Read each sentence.
Find the character that it describes.
Draw the symbol on the line.

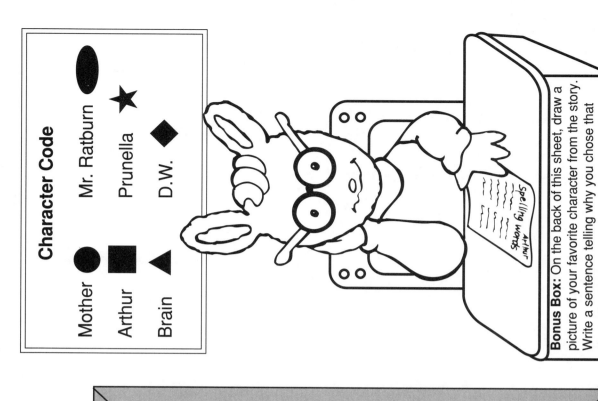

Character Code

Mother ●		Mr. Ratburn ⬤	
Arthur ■		Prunella ★	
Brain ▲		D.W. ◆	

1. I made chocolate chip cookies. _____

2. I am Arthur's sister. _____

3. I teach the kids in Room 13. _____

4. I missed the word FEAR. _____

5. I will go to Kindergarten next year. _____

6. We had the highest spelling scores in Room 13. _____

7. I won the spellathon last year. _____

8. I had the first turn in the spellathon. _____

9. We were the last two left in the spellathon. _____

10. I will teach Kindergarten next year. _____

11. I gave homework the first day of school. _____

12. I spelled PREPARATION to win the spellathon. _____

Bonus Box: On the back of this sheet, draw a picture of your favorite character from the story. Write a sentence telling why you chose that character.

7

Answer Key

1. ●
2. ◆
3. ⬬
4. ▲
5. ◆
6. ▲ ■
7. ★
8. ▲
9. ★ ■
10. ⬬
11. ⬬
12. ■

Pick A Prize

Read each sentence.
If the sentence is **true**, color the trophy **yellow**.
If the sentence is **not true**, color the trophy **green**.

Mr. Ratburn teaches in Room 15.

Arthur is in third grade.

Mr. Ratburn gave a test with one hundred words.

Mrs. Fink's class went to the aquarium.

Muffy was in the spellathon.

Buster had a good-luck charm.

D.W. goes to school.

Mr. Ratburn was proud of his class.

Prunella beat Arthur in the spellathon.

The spellathon was held in the auditorium.

Bonus Box: Arthur must have felt very proud to win the spellathon. Write a paragraph of 3–5 sentences about something you did that made you feel proud.

Award

Reproduce this award for students who have outstanding spelling scores or show progress with their spelling skills.

Congratulations!

_____

is an official member
of the
Super Spellers Club!

Mr. Ratburn
President, Super Spellers Club

Congratulations!

_____

is an official member
of the
Super Spellers Club!

Mr. Ratburn
President, Super Spellers Club

Answer Key

green	yellow	yellow	yellow	green
yellow	green	yellow	green	yellow

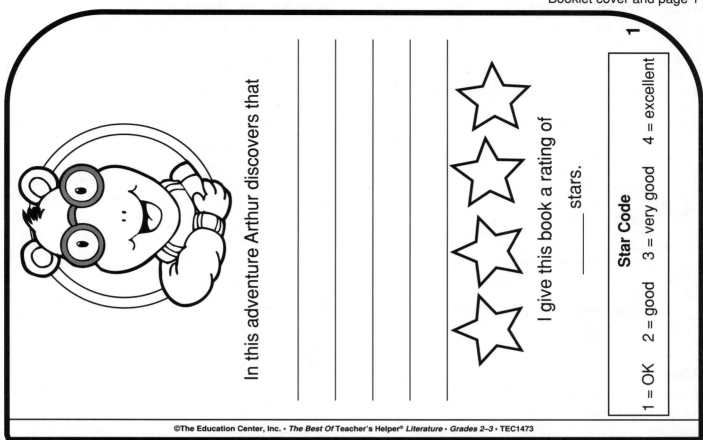

1

In this adventure Arthur discovers that

_____

_____

_____

_____

I give this book a rating of _____ stars.

Star Code

1 = OK   2 = good   3 = very good   4 = excellent

Presenting Arthur The Aardvark In...

How To Use The Literature Booklet (Pages 11–16)

The student activities on pages 11, 13, and 15 are designed so that they may be completed as a follow-up activity to any book in Marc Brown's An Arthur Adventure series.

How To Make Literature Booklets

1. Duplicate student copies of pages 11, 13, and 15 on white paper. You will also need one 7 1/4" x 10 1/4" sheet of white paper and one 9" x 12" sheet of light-colored construction paper per child.
2. Distribute the materials. Ask each student to cut on the bold outlines to create one booklet cover and five booklet pages.
3. Then, using the large sheet of white paper as the final booklet page, have each child sequence his cutouts and align the left edges. Demonstrate how to position the project atop the construction paper so that one-half inch of the construction paper extends from the left-hand side of the project. Staple each child's booklet together. Ask each child to fold the half-inch of construction paper over the stapled edge of his booklet and glue it in place. (See the illustration.)

How To Use Page 11 (The Booklet Cover And Page 1)

1. Have each student complete his booklet cover by coloring the Arthur illustration, then copying and illustrating the appropriate book title in the remaining area on the larger sheet of white paper. In the construction-paper margin, suggest that the student create a border of artwork that relates to the story, a technique used by author and illustrator Marc Brown. (See the illustration.)
2. On booklet page 1, have each student describe what Arthur discovers during his adventure. Then, using the star code at the bottom of the page, have each child rate the Arthur adventure by coloring the appropriate number of stars and filling in the blank.

Background For The Teacher
Marc Brown: 1946–

With paper, pencils, and encouragement provided by his grandmother and uncle—and close supervision from his high school art teacher—Marc Brown was determined to become an artist. Although impressed by many artists, Brown feels that Maurice Sendak's wonderfully illustrated book *Where The Wild Things Are* determined the course of his life.

Brown began his career illustrating textbooks. Eventually an editor encouraged him to write and illustrate children's books. Since that time, Brown has written and illustrated many books, including the ever-popular Arthur Adventure series. In his spare time, the author enjoys reading, gardening, and restoring antique houses. And he considers his red raspberry pie to be perhaps the best in the world!

Here a[re]
things that [happened]
in the story. [...] happened in t[...]

☆ 1.

☆ 2.

☆ 3.

☆ 4.

☆ 5.

3

©The Education Center, Inc. • *The Best Of* Teacher's Helper® *Literature* • *Grades 2–3* • TEC1473

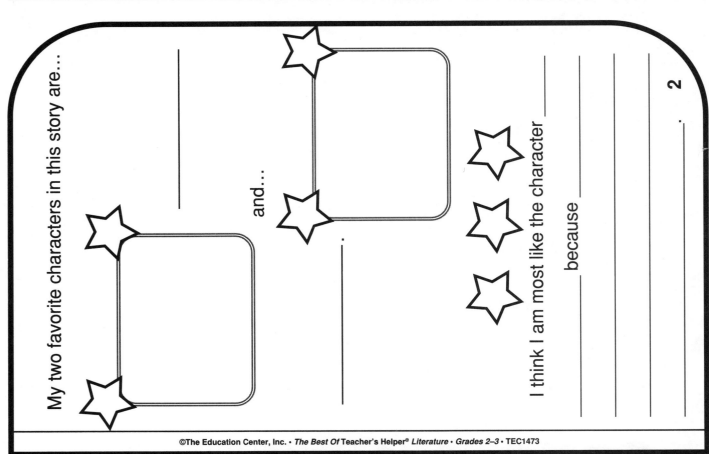

My two favorite characters in this story are...

and...

.

.

I think I am most like the character

because

.

2

©The Education Center, Inc. • *The Best Of* Teacher's Helper® *Literature* • *Grades 2–3* • TEC1473

How To Use Page 13
(Booklet Pages 2 And 3)

1. Ask each student to choose his two favorite characters from the Arthur adventure. Then, on page 2, have him illustrate each character in a box and write the characters' names on the corresponding lines. Next have each student complete the sentence on the page by determining which story character he is most like and why.

2. To complete booklet page 3, each student recalls five story events and writes the events in the order that they happened in the story.

5

This story about Arthur makes me think
about the time I _____
_____

Here's what happened: _____
_____
_____
_____
_____
_____
_____

Draw and color a picture of yourself in the box next to Arthur!

4

The best part of the story is when _____
_____
_____
_____
_____

Here is a picture that shows how it happens.

How To Use Page 15
(Booklet Pages 4 And 5)

1. To complete page 4, a student describes his favorite part of the Arthur adventure and illustrates it in the box.

2. On page 5 each student colors Arthur, then illustrates himself in the box with the famous story character. To complete the page, ask students what adventures from their own lives they thought about as they read or listened to Arthur's adventure. Have students use that information to complete the page.

Gila Monster Greetings

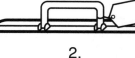

Read each sentence.
Choose the correct meaning for the underlined word.
Write the correct letter on the tag.

1.

The desert is so hot that you can <u>collapse</u>.

2.

Men were chasing the <u>buffaloes</u>.

3.

<u>Cactus</u> can live and grow with very little water.

4.

The cowboy wore a <u>bandanna</u> around his neck.

5.

A cactus was <u>underneath</u> the chair.

6.

A group of <u>gangsters</u> robbed the store.

7.

The boy will <u>probably</u> like his new home.

8.

I ate a <u>salami</u> sandwich for lunch.

9.

Firemen <u>rescue</u> people from burning buildings.

10.

The man wore a flower in his <u>lapel</u>.

11.

A <u>stampede</u> of horses ran past the barn.

12.

The <u>buzzards</u> flew around in circles.

---

a. birds that eat dead animals
b. the flap on the front of a coat or jacket
c. a large, colored handkerchief
d. spiny plants that grow in the desert

e. to fall down suddenly
f. a spiced, salted sausage
g. members of a criminal gang
h. wild oxen

i. a sudden rush of frightened animals
j. to save from danger
k. most likely
l. below

Background For The Teacher
Gila Monsters

Gila (HEE-luh) monsters are large lizards found in northern Mexico and in the deserts of the southwestern United States. Their skin is made up of beadlike bumps. Gila monsters are either brown or black and are marked with unusual patterns of orange, red, yellow, or white. These lizards grow to be between 18 and 23 inches long. They have wide bodies with short, broad tails. Gila monsters store fat in their tails, and they are able to live off this fat for several months if no food is available. They eat small animals and the eggs of birds and reptiles. The Gila monster and its relative, the Mexican beaded lizard, are the only poisonous lizards known to man.

Answer Key

1. e
2. h
3. d
4. c
5. l
6. g
7. k
8. f
9. j
10. b
11. i
12. a

Name _____

Whom To Believe?

Read each sentence below.
Decide if it tells about something make-believe or real.
Cut and paste each sentence in the correct column.

Alligators live in the sewers of New York City.

Gila monsters live out West in the hot desert.

Make-Believe	Real

Bonus Box: Choose one make-believe sentence and color a funny picture of it on the back of this sheet.

Boys can eat salami sandwiches.	Airplanes fly through bedrooms.
Spring and summer last only five minutes.	A taxi can drive you to a new house.
Everyone grows up to be a sheriff.	Kids can play baseball and ride bikes.
People can fly on airplanes.	Some books tell about Gila monsters and horned toads.
Baseball players chase stampeding buffaloes.	Alligators can meet you at the airport.

Answer Key

Make-Believe
Spring and summer last only five minutes.
Everyone grows up to be a sheriff.
Baseball players chase stampeding buffaloes.
Airplanes fly through bedrooms.
Alligators can meet you at the airport.

Real
Boys can eat salami sandwiches.
People can fly on airplanes.
A taxi can drive you to a new house.
Kids can play baseball and ride bikes.
Some books tell about Gila monsters and horned toads.

Cloudy Thoughts

Read each sentence.
If the sentence tells about something that happened in the story,
   color the cloud **yellow.**
If the sentence tells about something that did not happen in the story,
   color the cloud **blue.**

The boy and Seymour like to eat salami sandwiches.

The boy travels to the West by airplane.

Seymour rode his skateboard down the street.

Tex and Slim are taxi drivers.

There are Gila monsters and horned toads out West.

Buffaloes like to play baseball.

The boy will write a letter to his friend, Seymour.

Seymour visits the beach in California.

The boy sees children playing baseball.

Alligators live in the desert and eat cactus.

The boy in the cowboy hat has a pet horned toad.

The boy wanted to live in New York City forever.

Bonus Box: The boy plans to write his friend, Seymour, a letter about the West. Pretend you are the boy and write a letter to Seymour on the back of this sheet.

Answer Key

22

Name _____ *Gila Monsters Meet You At The Airport*
Recalling details

Cloudy Thoughts

Read each sentence.
If the sentence tells about something that happened in the story,
color the cloud **yellow.**
If the sentence tells about something that did not happen in the story,
color the cloud **blue.**

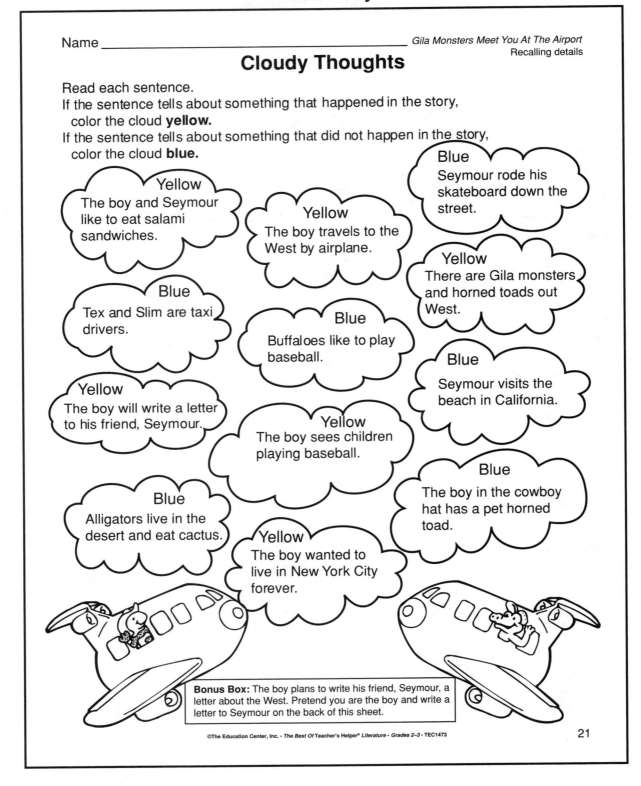

Yellow
The boy and Seymour like to eat salami sandwiches.

Yellow
The boy travels to the West by airplane.

Blue
Seymour rode his skateboard down the street.

Blue
Tex and Slim are taxi drivers.

Yellow
There are Gila monsters and horned toads out West.

Blue
Buffaloes like to play baseball.

Yellow
The boy will write a letter to his friend, Seymour.

Blue
Seymour visits the beach in California.

Yellow
The boy sees children playing baseball.

Blue
Alligators live in the desert and eat cactus.

Blue
The boy in the cowboy hat has a pet horned toad.

Yellow
The boy wanted to live in New York City forever.

Bonus Box: The boy plans to write his friend, Seymour, a letter about the West. Pretend you are the boy and write a letter to Seymour on the back of this sheet.

Huffing And Puffing

Read each sentence.
If the sentence is true, cut and glue a house to
  the correct box.
If the sentence is not true, cut and glue a broken-down
  house to the correct box.

1. The wolf ran out of sugar.

2. The wolf covered his mouth when he sneezed.

3. The wolf rang the doorbell at the stick house.

4. The wolf didn't eat the second little pig.

5. The second little pig was shaving when the wolf came to his door.

6. The third pig was smart.

7. The wolf delivered a birthday cake to his granny.

8. The police saw the wolf trying to break down the pig's door.

How To Use Pages 23, 25, 26, and 27

Duplicate pages 23, 25, 26, and 27 for your children. Read *The True Story Of The Three Little Pigs* by Jon Scieszka to your students. Allow students to voice their reactions to the wolf's story. Then have the children complete pages 23, 25, and 26. Before having students complete page 27, read a traditional version of *The Three Little Pigs* and encourage your children to discuss the differences and similarities between the two stories.

Answer Key

Huffing And Puffing

Read each sentence.
If the sentence is true, cut and glue a house to the correct box.
If the sentence is not true, cut and glue a broken-down house to the correct box.

1. The wolf ran out of sugar.

2. The wolf covered his mouth when he sneezed.

3. The wolf rang the doorbell at the stick house.

4. The wolf didn't eat the second little pig.

5. The second little pig was shaving when the wolf came to his door.

6. The third pig was smart.

7. The wolf delivered a birthday cake to his granny.

8. The police saw the wolf trying to break down the pig's door.

Name _____

You Be The Judge

JUDGE P. G. HAWG

Read each question.
Write your answer on the lines.

1. Do you believe the wolf's story? Explain your answer. _____
   _____
   _____

2. How do you think the first and second pigs felt when the wolf came to their homes? Why? _____
   _____
   _____

3. How do you think the third pig felt when the wolf came to his home? Why?
   _____
   _____

4. Do you think the wolf belongs in jail? Why or why not? _____
   _____
   _____

5. List three words to describe the third little pig. Explain why you chose each word. _____
   _____

6. What was your favorite part of the story? _____
   _____
   _____

Bonus Box: On the back of this page, draw a picture of the cake you think the wolf would have made for his granny.

Name _____

Try Again, Al!

Alexander T. Wolf is out of jail and back in his old neighborhood. He would like to be friends with the little pig that still lives there.

On the lines below, write a letter to Al telling him how to make friends with the third little pig.

date _____

Dear Al,

_____

_____

_____

_____

_____

_____

_____

_____

_____

_____

_____

Your friend,

_____

Bonus Box: On the back of this page, draw a picture of the wolf and the pig doing something together.

Name _____

New Neighbors

Compare and contrast an original story of *The Three Little Pigs* with *The True Story Of The Three Little Pigs.*

Read each sentence below.
If the sentence tells something that happened in both stories, cut and glue it to the house labeled *Same.*
If the sentence tells something that happened only in *The True Story Of The Three Little Pigs,* cut and glue it to the house labeled *Different.*

Different

Same

Bonus Box: If you were a little pig, what would you use to build your house? On the back of this sheet, draw a picture of the house you would build, and write a few sentences about it.

©The Education Center, Inc. • *The Best Of Teacher's Helper® Literature • Grades 2–3 •* TEC1473

The three pigs were brothers.	The wolf was baking a cake.	The pig said, "And your old granny can sit on a pin!"	The wolf said, "Little Pig, Little Pig, let me come in."	The police arrived.	The wolf blew down the house of sticks.
The wolf went to jail.	The wolf huffed and puffed.	The wolf couldn't blow down the house of bricks.	The wolf had a terrible cold.	The wolf blew down the house of straw.	The wolf wanted to borrow a cup of sugar.

27

How To Use Page 27

Duplicate page 27 for your students. Then read a traditional version of *The Three Little Pigs* to your youngsters. Have them discuss the differences and similarities between this story and *The True Story Of The Three Little Pigs* by Jon Scieszka. After your discussion, distribute the reproducibles to your children for completion.

Answer Key

Same			Different	
The three pigs were brothers.	The wolf said, "Little Pig, Little Pig, let me come in."		The wolf went to jail.	The wolf had a terrible cold.
The wolf huffed and puffed.	The wolf blew down the house of straw.		The wolf was baking a cake.	The police arrived.
The wolf couldn't blow down the house of bricks.	The wolf blew down the house of sticks.		The pig said, "And your old granny can sit on a pin!"	The wolf wanted to borrow a cup of sugar.

Name _____

That Is Quite Enough!

Read each sentence.
If it is a fact, color the polka dot pink.
If it is an opinion, color the polka dot green.

Bonus Box: Reread sentence number eight. On the back of this paper, write why you agree or disagree with this opinion.

1. Mr. Davis is the principal of Bailey Elementary School.

2. The third-grade students drove their last teacher crazy.

3. The new teacher, Mrs. Jeepers, is very mysterious.

4. Mrs. Jeepers has green eyes and red hair.

5. Her large green brooch is very pretty.

6. Mrs. Jeepers has a cool accent because she lived in Romania.

7. Mrs. Jeepers outlined three classroom rules.

8. Everyone knows that three classroom rules are not enough!

9. Mrs. Jeepers is probably a pushover.

10. The new teacher moved into the Clancy house.

11. The Clancy house is haunted!

12. Eddie likes to stir up trouble.

13. Eddie should be nice to Mrs. Jeepers.

14. Mrs. Jeepers ran her fingernails down the chalkboard.

15. She knew Eddie was the one who dropped the book.

16. Getting rid of Mrs. Jeepers will be easy.

How To Use This Literature Unit (Pages 29–34)

The student activities on pages 29, 31, and 33 are designed to accompany *Vampires Don't Wear Polka Dots,* one of a series of beginning chapter books written by Debbie Dadey and Marcia Thornton Jones. This book may be read aloud to students, or it may be read by students reading at a 3.0 or higher reading level.

How To Use Page 29

Use this activity after chapter 4 has been read.

Background For The Teacher
Debbie Dadey And Marcia Thornton Jones

This dynamic writing team began as teaching colleagues. Dadey was a librarian and Jones a classroom teacher. When the two discovered that they had a mutual dream of becoming published authors, they decided to join forces and work together toward their shared goal. For two years the pair routinely wrote during their lunch period—but with little success. Their turning point came when the writers were venting their frustrations about what a horrific day of teaching they had both just experienced. The more they vented, the sillier they got—until they had decided that the only way to corral their students' attention would be to grow horns, sprout fangs, blow smoke out of their ears, and grow to a height of 15 feet! This brainstorm paved the way to *Vampires Don't Wear Polka Dots,* a story about a mischievous group of third-grade students who suspect that their new teacher is a vampire. Since that first book, there's been no stopping this writing duo! The authors' somewhat naughty group of student characters are now the infamous Bailey School kids—and you just never know what those kids (or authors) are going to be thinking up next!

More Bailey School Kid Adventures
(Available from Scholastic Inc.)

Leprechauns Don't Play Basketball
Santa Claus Doesn't Mop Floors
Werewolves Don't Go To Summer Camp
Ghosts Don't Eat Potato Chips
Frankenstein Doesn't Plant Petunias
Aliens Don't Wear Braces
Genies Don't Ride Bicycles
Pirates Don't Wear Pink Sunglasses
Witches Don't Do Backflips
Skeletons Don't Play Tubas
Cupid Doesn't Flip Hamburgers
Gremlins Don't Chew Bubble Gum

Answer Key

1. pink/fact
2. green/opinion
3. green/opinion
4. pink/fact
5. green/opinion
6. green/opinion
7. pink/fact
8. green/opinion
9. green/opinion
10. pink/fact
11. green/opinion
12. pink/fact
13. green/opinion
14. pink/fact
15. pink/fact
16. green/opinion

Name _____

Color the house.
Cut on the dotted lines.
Arrange the events in order.

The Dare

©The Education Center, Inc. • *The Best Of* Teacher's Helper® *Literature* • Grades 2–3 • TEC1473

Glue here.

Eddie and Melody meet at the streetlight.	Eddie opens the basement door.
They run out of the basement.	A woman steps out the front door.
Eddie and Melody tell what happened.	Eddie agrees to sneak into the basement.
Mrs. Jeepers mentions the prowlers.	Melody decides to go with Eddie.
An upstairs light comes on.	They find the long wooden box.
Mrs. Jeepers stares at Eddie and Melody.	They creep down the basement steps.
There is a loud thump.	The lid on the box won't budge.

To finish the project:

1. Glue the house to the top edge of your colored paper.
2. Below the house, glue the events in order.
3. Write your name at the bottom of the project.

How To Use Page 31

Duplicate page 31 on white construction paper for each student. Use the activity after chapter 9 has been read.

Materials Needed For Page 31

— markers or crayons
— scissors
— glue
— a 4 1/2" x 12" strip of colored construction paper for each
   student

Answer Key

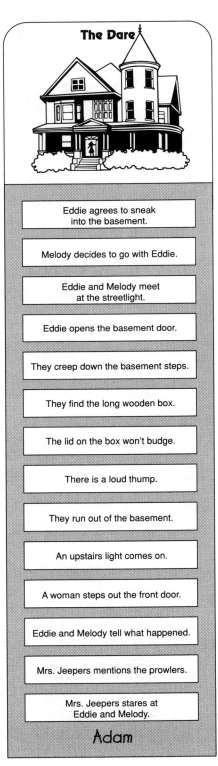

Colorful Characters

Think about the three story characters shown.
Use the code below to color the frames.
Finish the sentences.

I think Mrs. Jeepers was
_____
because in the story
_____
_____
_____ .

I think Eddie was
_____
because in the story
_____
_____
_____ .

I think Melody was
_____
because in the story
_____
_____
_____ .

Draw an illustration in each box.
Use the code to color the frames.
Finish the sentences.

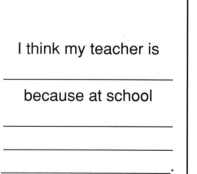

I think my teacher is
_____
because at school
_____
_____
_____ .

I think I am
_____
because at school
_____
_____
_____ .

I think my friend is
_____
because at school
_____
_____
_____ .

Color Code

brave	= orange	smart	= purple	inconsiderate	= gray
friendly	= red	unique	= yellow	thoughtful	= blue
creative	= green	popular	= pink	honest	= gold

How To Use Page 33

Use this activity after the story has been completed.

JUMPING TO CONCLUSIONS

Strip A

Finished Project

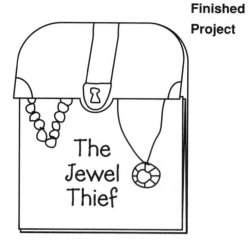

AN ALI BABA ADVENTURE

Ali Baba's Evidence

What Ali Baba Thinks Happens

Strip B

Glue to Strip A.

What Actually Happens

What Ali Baba Didn't Know

by _____

©The Education Center, Inc.

How To Use This Literature Unit
Pages 35–40

The student activities on pages 35, 37, and 39 are designed to accompany *The Adventures Of Ali Baba Bernstein*—a chapter book by Johanna Hurwitz.

Materials Needed
— white construction-paper copy of page 35
— pencil
— scissors
— glue
— crayons or markers

How To Use Page 35

1. Use this activity after chapter 2 has been read.
2. Remind students that in chapter 2, Ali Baba jumps to the conclusion that Mr. Vivaldi is a jewel thief. Ask students to recall the evidence on which Ali Baba bases his conclusion and write it under the heading "Ali Baba's Evidence."
3. Under the heading "What Ali Baba Thinks Happens," have students describe how Ali Baba thinks Mr. Vivaldi is stealing jewels.
4. Next ask students to describe what really happened and what Ali Baba didn't know—but found out later—in the appropriate spaces on their papers. Help students understand that if Ali Baba had gathered sufficient evidence, he would not have jumped to the conclusion that Mr. Vivaldi was a jewel thief.
5. To complete the activity and create the chest of jewels pictured, have each child cut on the bold lines and glue the two resulting cutouts together where indicated.
6. While the glue is drying, have each student fold forward the top and bottom sections of his project along the thin lines, then program and decorate the blank surfaces to resemble the chest of jewels pictured on page 35.
7. When the glue is dry, demonstrate how to make the accordion folds along the remaining thin lines.

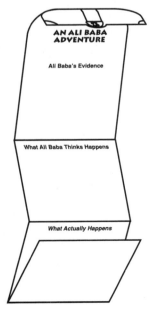

Story Summary
The Adventures Of Ali Baba Bernstein
By Johanna Hurwitz

Eight-year-old David Bernstein is determined to make life more interesting. And changing his name just might do the trick! After all, it's a pain having four Davids in his third-grade classroom, and it's also a major bore that there are 17 listings for David Bernstein in the Manhattan phone directory. So David begins calling himself Ali Baba Bernstein and asks that his parents, teacher, and classmates do the same. Can an exciting name lead to exciting adventures? In Ali Baba Bernstein's case, it most certainly does!

Background For The Teacher
Johanna Hurwitz: 1937–

As a nine-year-old child, Johanna Hurwitz had two ambitions in life: to become a librarian and to write books. Today she has fulfilled both of these desires—but it wasn't easy. Hurwitz began working for the New York Public Library while still a high school student. By 1959 she had become a full-fledged librarian, but it wasn't until 1977 that her first book for children was published. Understandably, finding time to write while raising two children was a challenge. In addition, Hurwitz admits that being a children's librarian might have inhibited her early writing efforts—what could she possibly have to say that hadn't already been written in a book somewhere? Eventually Hurwitz got an idea for a short story that was so strong she didn't even stop to wonder if anyone had written about it before. That tiny story featured a character called Nora *(Busybody Nora, Nora And Mrs. Mind-Your-Own-Business)*.

It usually takes Hurwitz about six months to write a book. The author admits that in all of her books of fiction, there are some incidents that have really happened. She also concedes that when she hears a name she likes, she writes the name on a slip of paper and tosses it into her "name drawer." These are often the names that she chooses for her book characters.

Children and teachers may write to the author in care of her publishing company. As a courtesy to the author, it's best to send either one letter from the class or to package individual student letters in a single, large envelope. Mail correspondence to:

Johanna Hurwitz
c/o Morrow Junior Books
1350 Avenue Of The Americas
New York, NY 10019

Answer Key
(Answers will vary, but should include the following information.)

Ali Baba's Evidence
The trunk labeled "Vivaldi" is filled with diamonds, rubies, pearls, and gold chains.
Ali Baba hears a woman's screams coming from Mr. Vivaldi's apartment.

What Ali Baba Thinks Happens
Mr. Vivaldi lures women into his apartment and steals their jewels.

What Actually Happens
The woman's screams are an opera recording.
The jewelry in the trunk is fake.

What Ali Baba Didn't Know
Mr. Vivaldi used to sing with the opera. He kept the costumes and jewelry that he wore on stage.

KIDNAPPED!

Read each sentence.
If it is a **fact,** color the circle in the fact column.
If it is an **opinion,** color the circle in the opinion column.

fact	opinion	
Ⓜ	Ⓗ	1. Ali Baba spends the afternoon with Roger.
Ⓢ	Ⓕ	2. Roger's mom leaves the apartment.
Ⓝ	Ⓞ	3. Roger's mom should have taken the baby.
Ⓣ	Ⓐ	4. The boys play a computer game.
Ⓛ	Ⓥ	5. Computer games are lots of fun.
Ⓢ	Ⓤ	6. Sugar is a really cute baby.
Ⓑ	Ⓘ	7. When Ali Baba looks in Sugar's crib, she is gone.
Ⓟ	Ⓑ	8. Roger calls his mother on the phone.
Ⓔ	Ⓚ	9. The kidnappers probably wore black clothes.
Ⓒ	Ⓦ	10. The door to the apartment is locked.
Ⓣ	Ⓓ	11. All kidnappers should be good at picking locks.
Ⓕ	Ⓚ	12. Roger and Ali Baba search the house.
Ⓠ	Ⓡ	13. Sugar is found!
Ⓞ	Ⓢ	14. It was silly to think that Sugar had been kidnapped.
Ⓧ	Ⓥ	15. The boys should tell Roger's mother what happened.

Crack the coded message.
For each number, write the letter that **is not** colored.

$$\overline{10}\ \overline{1}\ \overline{4}\ \overline{11}\quad \overline{10}\ \overline{7}\ \overline{5}\ \overline{5}$$

$$\overline{4}\ \overline{5}\ \overline{7}\quad \overline{8}\ \overline{4}\ \overline{8}\ \overline{4}\quad \overline{8}\ \overline{9}\ \overline{13}\ \overline{3}\ \overline{6}\ \overline{11}\ \overline{9}\ \overline{3}$$

$$\overline{11}\ \overline{1}\ \overline{7}\ \overline{3}\ \overline{12}\quad \overline{14}\ \overline{2}\quad \overline{3}\ \overline{9}\ \overline{15}\ \overline{11}\ ?$$

Bonus Box: Would you like to have Ali Baba as your friend? On the back of this paper, write your answer; then explain why you would or would not like to be friends with Ali Baba.

Answer Key

1. fact
2. fact
3. opinion
4. fact
5. opinion
6. opinion
7. fact
8. fact
9. opinion
10. fact
11. opinion
12. fact
13. fact
14. opinion
15. opinion

WHAT WILL
ALI BABA BERNSTEIN
THINK OF NEXT?

Name _____

THE MANY SIDES OF ALI BABA

brave
shows courage

unique
is one of a kind

imaginative
has lots of
imagination

suspicious
doubts or
suspects

curious
is eager to find
out new things

superstitious
believes in things like unlucky
numbers and magic spells

1. David changed his name to Ali Baba because he likes being
_____.

2. Only a very _____ eight-year-old would visit a
suspected jewel thief!

3. Ali Baba was _____ of Eddie Whitestone
because he thought Eddie had something up his sleeve.

4. It was very _____ of Ali Baba to think that
kidnappers stole Sugar.

5. Ali Baba must be _____ if he thinks a magic
spell will get rid of his wart.

6. Ali Baba is very _____ about the other David
Bernsteins, so he invites all of them to his birthday party.

Materials Needed For Each Student

— white construction-paper copy of page 39
— pencil
— scissors
— six 5 1/2" x 7 1/4" white construction-paper booklet pages
— access to a stapler
— glue
— crayons or markers

How To Use Page 39

1. Use this activity after the entire book has been read.
2. As a class, read and discuss each of the character traits defined on page 39.
3. Have each student complete the sentences on his paper by writing the most appropriate character trait in each blank.
4. Ask a different student volunteer to read aloud each completed sentence. Discuss any discrepancies.
5. Instruct each student to cut on the bold lines, creating one booklet cover and six programmed strips.
6. Have each student glue one programmed paper strip on each blank booklet page. While the glue dries, have each student illustrate her booklet pages with pictures that tell about the parts of the story to which the programming refers.
7. After each student personalizes and colors her booklet cover, she staples her booklet pages in order behind her completed cover.

Follow-Up Activity

Invite students to create similar booklets about themselves! To do this, provide each student with a construction-paper booklet that has a cover and six blank pages. Each student illustrates herself on the cover of her booklet, then lists and defines six self-describing character traits. On each booklet page, she writes and illustrates a sentence that provides an example of one character trait shown on her booklet cover. Be sure to set aside time for students to share these autobiographical works!

More Books About Ali Baba

Hurray For Ali Baba Bernstein
Morrow Junior Books, 1989

Nine-year-old Ali Baba—who has just started fourth grade—is back for another round of unusual, funny adventures, which include staying at home unsupervised and investigating the unusual habits of his neighbor Mr. Salmon. A brief meeting with perhaps the "real" Santa Claus (in disguise, of course!) has Ali Baba, who celebrates Hanukkah, and his friend Natalie, who celebrates Christmas, chatting with the white-haired gentleman about his gift-giving practices.

Ali Baba Bernstein, Lost And Found
Morrow Junior Books, 1992

Ali Baba is almost ten years old and his life is as exciting as ever! In this hilarious sequel, Ali Baba scopes out a "bomb" in the movie theater, hunts for bears during the Bernsteins' summer vacation, and tries to convince his folks that he's responsible enough to own a pet.

Answer Key
1. unique
2. brave
3. suspicious
4. imaginative
5. superstitious
6. curious

Name _____

"Key" Clues

Read the definition on each key.
Cut out and glue the matching word to each key.

Clues to missing key...

Vocabulary words:

eel

detective

doormat

drainpipe

deposit

alley

slunk

license

case

jingles

hunks

collect

a narrow
street
between
buildings

large
pieces

a mat
used to
wipe off
feet

moves
with a
clinking
sound

a problem
for a detec-
tive to solve

a person
who solves
cases

a tube
used to
carry off
water

a metal
dog tag

to put
money in
a bank

to have
moved in a
sneaky way

a long,
slippery,
snakelike
fish

to save or
gather
together

Bonus Box: You have been given a magical key that can unlock any door.
Write a story on handwriting paper telling about your adventures.

©The Education Center, Inc. • *The Best Of Teacher's Helper® Literature • Grades 2–3* • TEC1473

41

Author Profile: Marjorie Weinman Sharmat

Ms. Sharmat started writing when she was eight, in a joint-effort newspaper. It reached a circulation of four: her parents and the parents of her writing partner! With her parents' encouragement, she continued to write anything from diaries and poems to a first chapter of a mystery novel. Ms. Sharmat's first published piece was a four-word advertising slogan. When her first story was published, it caused her to break out in hives. She now regards red blotches as a sign of literary achievement!

Ms. Sharmat became interested in children's literature upon the birth of her two sons. Preferring to write about people, she is often inspired by her family. Ms. Sharmat cares deeply about the reactions of her readers and hopes to please. Her avid audience proves that she has accomplished her goal.

Extension Activity
Key Clues For School

Duplicate copies of the key pattern below onto tagboard. Program the keys with clues to specific places in your school, to school personnel, or to other school-related topics. Program answers on the backs of the keys. Laminate and cut out. Using a hole punch, punch holes where indicated and place the keys on a metal ring. When you have a few minutes to spare, read the clues from one of the keys. Your young detectives will delight in solving these school mysteries!

Pattern

Answer Key

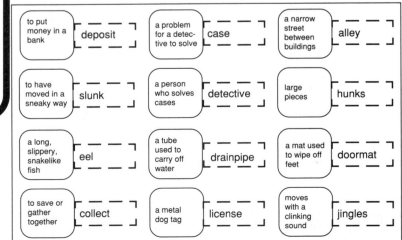

Clue	Answer	Clue	Answer	Clue	Answer
to put money in a bank	deposit	a problem for a detective to solve	case	a narrow street between buildings	alley
to have moved in a sneaky way	slunk	a person who solves cases	detective	large pieces	hunks
a long, slippery, snakelike fish	eel	a tube used to carry off water	drainpipe	a mat used to wipe off feet	doormat
to save or gather together	collect	a metal dog tag	license	moves with a clinking sound	jingles

Boning Up On Details

Read each sentence.
If the sentence is true, circle the
   letter under true.
If the sentence is false, circle the
   letter under false.

	True	False
1. Annie leaves her key on the desk.	S	E
2. Nate writes a note to Annie.	O	S
3. The first place Nate looks is the drainpipe.	I	B
4. Nate looks at a garbage can in the alley.	E	N
5. Nate is afraid of Fang.	T	D
6. Rosamond has three black cats.	A	T
7. Nate is happy that Oliver helps with the case.	N	S
8. Annie's mother and father do not like dog parties.	E	P
9. Rosamond writes a strange poem.	H	R
10. Nate does not want to see the eels.	P	C
11. Oliver finds the key on Fang's collar.	Y	T

What is a good nickname for Oliver?

To find the answer, write the circled letter from each sentence
above on the matching numbered blank below.

___ ___ ___   ___ ___ ___ ___   ___ ___ ___ ___
 5   9   1   3   8   2 11   10   4   7   6

Bonus Box: On the back of this sheet, draw a picture of your favorite part of
the story. Write a sentence telling why this is your favorite part.

Answer Key

	True	False
1.	S	(E)
2.	O	(S)
3.	I	(B)
4.	(E)	N
5.	(T)	D
6.	A	(T)
7.	N	(S)
8.	(E)	P
9.	(H)	R
10.	(P)	C
11.	Y	(T)

Answer to riddle:
The best pest!

Grading The Great

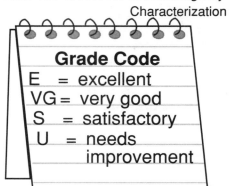

Grade Code

E	=	excellent
VG	=	very good
S	=	satisfactory
U	=	needs improvement

Complete each character's report card.
Draw in the character's face.
Write a grade in each box to show what the character is like.
Use the grade code.

Nate

☐ Curious

☐ Hard worker

☐ Dependable

☐ Gets along with others

Comments: _____

_____

_____

Annie

☐ Curious

☐ Hard worker

☐ Dependable

☐ Gets along with others

Comments: _____

_____

_____

Oliver

☐ Curious

☐ Hard worker

☐ Dependable

☐ Gets along with others

Comments: _____

_____

_____

Rosamond

☐ Curious

☐ Hard worker

☐ Dependable

☐ Gets along with others

Comments: _____

_____

_____

Literature Enrichment

Encourage your students to read other Nate The Great stories such as:

Nate The Great
Nate The Great And The Boring Beach Bag
Nate The Great And The Lost List
Nate The Great And The Phony Clue
Nate The Great And The Snowy Trail
Nate The Great And The Sticky Case
Nate The Great Goes Undercover
Nate The Great Stalks Stupidweed

Bookmark

Reproduce copies of this bookmark on colorful construction paper for students completing *Nate The Great And The Missing Key*. Punch the bookmarks for each Nate The Great title the students read. Reward students who read five or more titles with stickers.

Nate the Great

name

©The Education Center, Inc.

Summertime Refreshment

Read each word meaning.
Write the matching word on the line.
Use the Word Bank.

1.
_____
to guide
an object

2.
_____
very bad

3.
_____
a baby frog or
toad

4.
_____
splash with
drops of liquid

5.
_____
very good

6.
_____
to be held or
captured

7.
_____
the day after
today

8.
_____
lovely

9.
_____
a grassy area

10.
_____
to make
something
pretty

Word Bank

beautiful   splatter

caught   steer

decorate   terrible

meadow   tomorrow

pollywog   wonderful

Bonus Box: Frog and Toad ate chocolate ice cream together.
On the back of this sheet, write a sentence telling what flavor
of ice cream you would like to share with a friend and why.

Summertime Refreshment

Read each sentence.
If the sentence is true, color the leaf green.
If the sentence is false, color the leaf brown.

Toad was alone on the sled.

Toad was the big brown thing covered with sticks and leaves.

Frog did not have any winter clothes.

Frog went to the store for ice-cream cones.

The birthday present was a clock.

Frog and Toad ate chocolate ice-cream cones on a cold winter's day.

Toad's clock was broken.

Toad and Frog like chocolate ice-cream cones.

Frog bought Toad a present.

Frog saw his mother and father working in their garden.

Frog raked the leaves on Toad's lawn.

Spring was around the corner of Toad's house.

Frog decorated the Christmas tree.

Bonus Box: On the back of this sheet, write three sentences telling about something nice you did for someone else and how it made you feel.

Roly-Poly Puppet

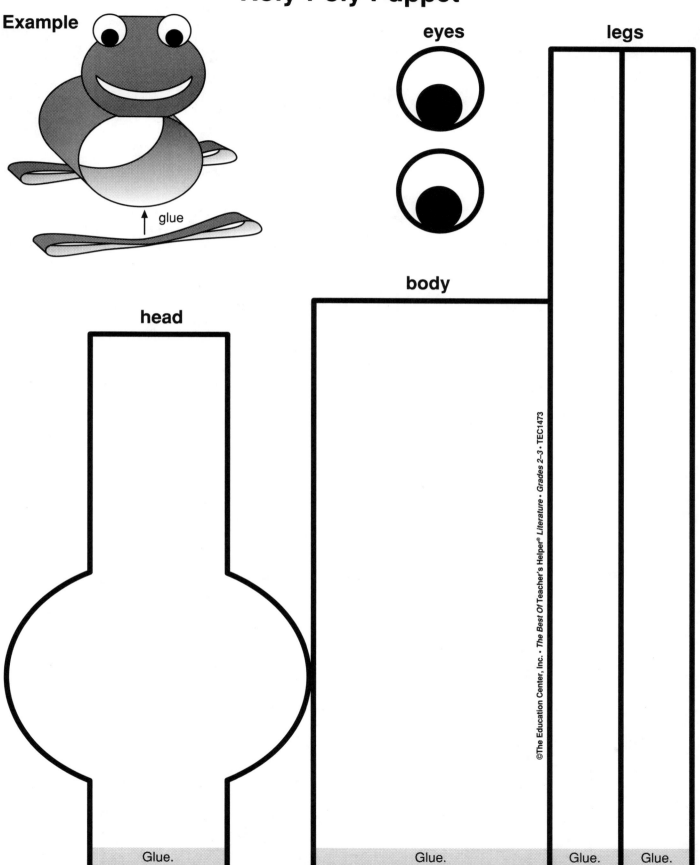

Example

glue

eyes

legs

body

head

©The Education Center, Inc. • *The Best Of Teacher's Helper® Literature • Grades 2–3 • TEC1473*

Glue.

Glue.

Glue.

Glue.

Frog And Toad All Year
By Arnold Lobel

Who can resist the silly antics of Frog and Toad? Upon finishing this book, be sure to share the following titles with your Frog and Toad fans:

Days With Frog & Toad
Frog & Toad Are Friends
The Frog & Toad Pop-Up Book
Frog & Toad Together

Answer Key
Page 47

1. steer
2. terrible
3. pollywog
4. splatter
5. wonderful
6. caught
7. tomorrow
8. beautiful
9. meadow
10. decorate

How To Use Page 49

Provide students with white construction-paper copies of page 49. Have each student decide whether he will make a Frog or a Toad puppet. Have students complete their puppets by following the directions below. Challenge student pairs to write new adventures for Frog and Toad. Have willing student pairs present their stories to the class using their puppets. Hop to it!

Materials Needed

— scissors
— crayons
— glue
— construction-paper scraps

Directions For The Students

1. Color your puppet's legs, body, and head green for Frog or brown for Toad.
2. Cut out the puppet pieces along the bold lines.
3. To create the puppet's body, roll the body piece into a loop and glue where indicated. Set aside.
4. To create the puppet's legs, roll each leg piece into a loop and glue where indicated.
5. Glue each leg loop in the middle as shown; then glue it onto the body.
6. To create the head, roll the head piece into a loop and glue where indicated.
7. Glue the head onto the top of the body.
8. Glue the eyes onto the head.
9. Add a construction-paper mouth.
10. Place your hand inside the puppet's body to make your Frog or Toad hop!

Answer Key
Page 48

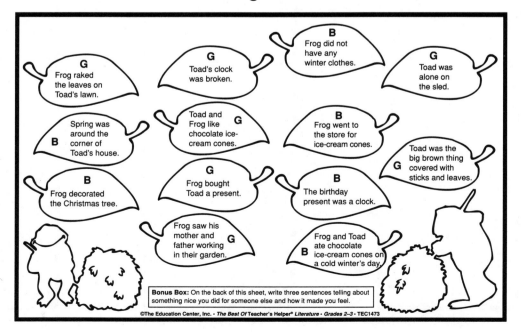

G Frog raked the leaves on Toad's lawn.

G Toad's clock was broken.

B Frog did not have any winter clothes.

G Toad was alone on the sled.

B Spring was around the corner of Toad's house.

G Toad and Frog like chocolate ice-cream cones.

B Frog went to the store for ice-cream cones.

G Toad was the big brown thing covered with sticks and leaves.

B Frog decorated the Christmas tree.

G Frog bought Toad a present.

B The birthday present was a clock.

G Frog saw his mother and father working in their garden.

B Frog and Toad ate chocolate ice-cream cones on a cold winter's day.

Bonus Box: On the back of this sheet, write three sentences telling about something nice you did for someone else and how it made you feel.

Pick A Paintbrush

Read each sentence.
Choose the correct meaning of the bold word as it
   is used in the story.
Color the paintbrush.

1. The wise **shaman** spoke to Little Gopher.

medicine man   father

2. An Indian **maiden** came out of the clouds.

young lady   colt

3. Little Gopher saw his **vision** in the sky.

face   something seen in a dream

4. Little Gopher painted a white **buckskin**.

soft leather   sheet

5. Little Gopher **longed** to share his Dream-Vision.

wished   decided

6. The **warriors** brought animal skins back from the hunt.

leaders   fighting men

7. Little Gopher found the colors he was **seeking**.

stirring   looking for

8. Little Gopher painted pictures of the warriors' **deeds**.

acts of courage   land

9. The hill was **ablaze** with color.

glowing   surrounded by

10. The brushes **multiplied** into many plants.

mixed   increased in number

11. The hills and meadows **burst** into bloom.

appeared suddenly   started

12. Little Gopher followed the **customs** of his tribe.

usual habits   trails

Bonus Box: On the back of this sheet, color a picture of a beautiful sunset.

How To Use This Unit

Read the book *The Legend Of The Indian Paintbrush* by Tomie dePaola to your class. Lead your students in a discussion about the story. Then duplicate pages 51, 53, 55, and 57 for each of your students to complete. Use the literature-unit planning sheet on page 59 to help you plan further literature experiences.

Background For The Teacher
Plains Indians

The Native Americans referred to as the Plains Indians included many different tribes. These tribes lived in a similar region of the country and they shared, to some extent, a similar way of life. Languages among the Plains Indians differed from tribe to tribe. Some of the Plains Indians are listed below.

— **The Pawnee** farmed *maize* (Indian corn) and were located west of the Missouri River in the area we now call Nebraska.

— **The Sauk and Fox** lived together as a single tribe in the Iowa area. They lived in dome-shaped huts covered with birch bark, rushes, or mats.

— **The Mandan** lived in the Missouri River/Dakota territory. They farmed and hunted for their food and clothing. They lived in sturdy, round earthen huts. They lived near the river and made boats called *bullboats* by stretching buffalo hides over wooden frames.

— **The Osage** lived in areas of Arkansas, Missouri, and Oklahoma. They were hunters.

— **The Iroquois** lived in the area east of the Great Lakes and were mainly farmers.

— **The Sioux** were hunters and nomads who lived in the South Dakota area. Their homes were tents called *teepees,* which were easily moved from place to place.

Before the horse was introduced as an animal for riding, some of the Plains Indians hunted buffalo in wolf disguises. The hunters covered themselves in wolf skins and moved toward a herd. Buffalo usually did not run from wolves, which allowed the hunters to move close to the buffalo and shoot several arrows. In this manner, they were able to obtain the meat and hides needed for their existence.

Answer Key

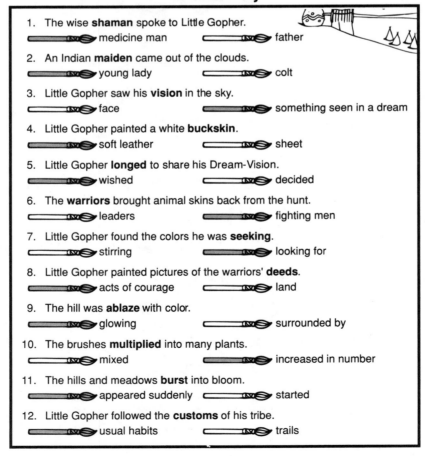

1. The wise **shaman** spoke to Little Gopher.
   medicine man   father

2. An Indian **maiden** came out of the clouds.
   young lady   colt

3. Little Gopher saw his **vision** in the sky.
   face   something seen in a dream

4. Little Gopher painted a white **buckskin**.
   soft leather   sheet

5. Little Gopher **longed** to share his Dream-Vision.
   wished   decided

6. The **warriors** brought animal skins back from the hunt.
   leaders   fighting men

7. Little Gopher found the colors he was **seeking**.
   stirring   looking for

8. Little Gopher painted pictures of the warriors' **deeds**.
   acts of courage   land

9. The hill was **ablaze** with color.
   glowing   surrounded by

10. The brushes **multiplied** into many plants.
    mixed   increased in number

11. The hills and meadows **burst** into bloom.
    appeared suddenly   started

12. Little Gopher followed the **customs** of his tribe.
    usual habits   trails

Links Of A Legend

Write one story event on each strip.

glue	*The Legend Of The Indian Paintbrush* by Tomie dePaola Name _____
glue	_____ _____
glue	_____ _____
glue	_____ _____
glue	_____ _____
glue	_____ _____
glue	_____ _____

Make a story chain.
Cut out the strips.
Glue the strips in order like a chain.
Start with the title.

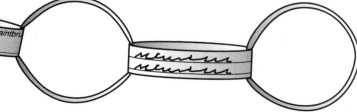

Background For The Teacher
Tomie dePaola

Tomie dePaola (de-*pow*-la) is among the most prolific authors of self-illustrated children's books. He says he made the decision to become an artist and author of books when he was four. After graduating from Pratt Institute in 1956, dePaola spent six months in a Benedictine monastery where he says he was "sort of the resident artist." About his art style, dePaola says, "…I'm drawn to Romanesque and folk art. I think that my style is very close to those—very simple and direct. I simplify." Tomie dePaola says his dream is to have one of his books touch some individual child and change that child's life for the better.

Tomie dePaola Booklist

The Art Lesson (Putnam Publishing Group, 1989)

Bill And Pete (Putnam Publishing Group, 1978)

The Cloud Book (Holiday House, Inc.; 1975)

Fin M'Coul, The Giant Of Knockmany Hill (Holiday House, Inc.; 1981)

The Legend Of Old Befana (Harcourt Brace Jovanovich, 1980)

The Legend Of The Bluebonnet (Retold by Tomie dePaola, Putnam Publishing Group, 1983)

Nana Upstairs And Nana Downstairs (Puffin Books, 1978)

Now One Foot, Now The Other (Putnam Publishing Group, 1981)

Pancakes For Breakfast (Harcourt Brace Jovanovich, 1978)

The Popcorn Book (Holiday House, Inc.; 1978)

Strega Nona (Simon & Schuster Trade, 1979)

Watch Out For The Chicken Feet In Your Soup (Simon & Schuster Trade, 1974)

Design A Sign

Make a sign that could be placed near a field of Indian Paintbrushes.
On the sign, retell the legend of the Indian Paintbrush so that visitors will know how this plant received its name.

_____
Sign Title

_____

_____

_____

_____

_____

_____

_____

Sign Maker _____

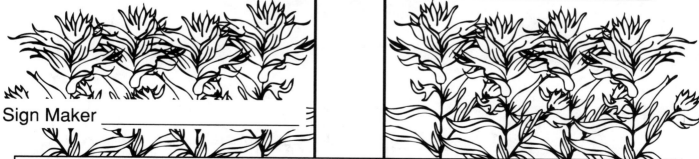

Bonus Box: Draw a picture of your favorite flower on the back of this sheet. Below the picture, write a legend about how the flower got its name.

Extension Activity
Art Project/Bulletin-Board Display

Duplicate the framed buckskin below onto tan or white construction paper for each of your students. Provide colored chalk for your children and have each child create his own "Dream-Vision" picture. Spray each completed picture with hairspray to keep the chalk from smearing. Display the completed projects on a bulletin board titled "Our Dream-Visions."

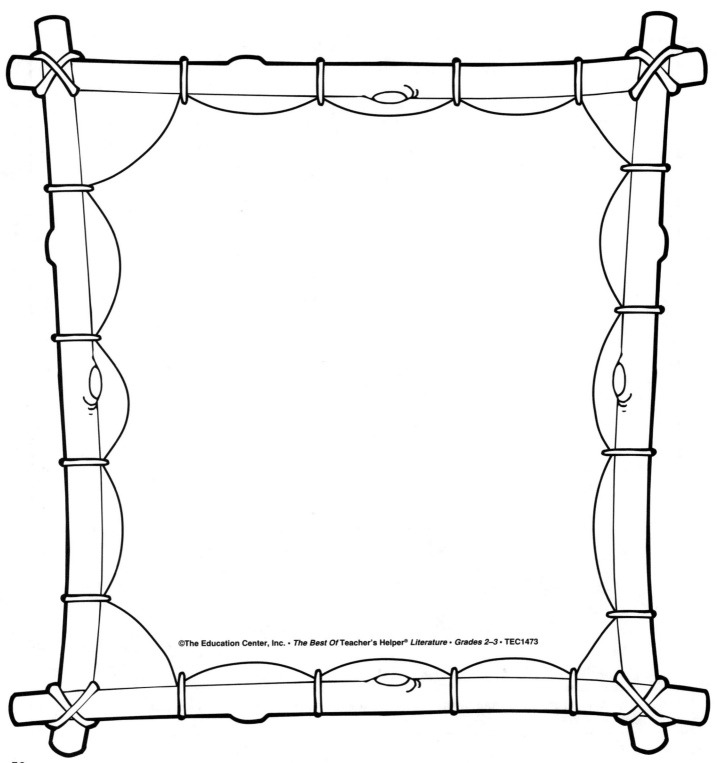

©The Education Center, Inc. • *The Best Of* Teacher's Helper® *Literature* • *Grades 2–3* • TEC1473

Tell It Like It Is

Follow the directions.

Name the main character(s).

_____

Would you rate this story excellent, good, or poor? Tell why.

_____

Draw a picture of your favorite part of the story.

Write about what happened in the story.

How To Use Page 57

Duplicate page 57 for each of your students. Have each child reflect on the story *The Legend Of The Indian Paintbrush* by Tomie dePaola. Then have him follow the directions in each box. Use this page when having your students evaluate books in your future literature units.

Literature-Unit Planning Sheet

Name Of Unit: _____

Creative-Writing Activities

Culminating Activities

Critical-Thinking Questions

Independent Student Activities

Across-The-Curriculum Activities

Teacher-Directed Activities

Field-Trip Options

How To Use Page 59

Use this chart to help plan your literature units throughout the school year. Duplicate a copy of page 59 for each literature unit. By listing all of your book-related activities and information, your literature units will be organized and hassle-free. For assistance in planning your literature units, refer to the sample page below. If desired, record vocabulary activities and bulletin-board ideas on the back of each page. File each planning sheet and other valuable information for future use.

Literature-Unit Planning Sheet

Name Of Unit: **The Legend Of The Indian Paintbrush**

Teacher-Directed Activities

—Have students brainstorm the advantages and disadvantages of Little Gopher being a warrior or an artist. (List responses.)

—Make a class big book by retelling the story or creating new characters for the story. Have students create illustrations.

Critical-Thinking Questions

—How do you think Little Gopher felt when he saw the Dream-Vision?

—Why do you think Little Gopher wished he could be a warrior?

—If you lived with Little Gopher's people, would you want to be a warrior or an artist? Why?

Independent Student Activities

—Read and evaluate other books by Tomie dePaola.

Creative-Writing Activities

—Write legends.

—Write stories: "If I Lived With Little Gopher's People."

—Write about dreams.

—Write about unique talents you have.

Field-Trip Options

—Visit Indian ruins.

—Visit Native American museum.

—Visit zoo to see buffalo.

Across-The-Curriculum Activities

—Study the Plains Indians.

—Math and story problems with Native American themes.

—Study plants and flowers.

—Identify the locations of the Plains Indians on a U.S. map.

Culminating Activities

—Painting sunsets (watercolors on buckskin cutouts)

Oh No, It's The Swamp!

Read each sentence.
Match the underlined word to a definition.
Write each number on the correct desk.

	Definitions
Miss Nelson's class was <u>relieved</u>.	1. a person who takes the place of another
The children thought that Miss Swamp was the meanest <u>substitute</u> in the whole world.	2. showed
Three of the <u>ringleaders</u> of 207 came up with a plan.	3. uneasy or worried
"I <u>shall</u> teach this class," said Mr. Blandsworth.	4. pretending to be someone else
Mr. Blandsworth showed the children his <u>corny</u> card tricks.	5. no longer worried or upset
Someone was <u>impersonating</u> Miss Nelson.	6. the leaders of the trouble-makers
The children were very <u>nervous</u>.	7. will
The children <u>tottered</u> into the room dressed like Miss Nelson.	8. wobbled
Mr. Blandsworth tried to <u>amuse</u> the class.	9. to entertain in a playful way
Mr. Blandsworth <u>demonstrated</u> bird calls for the children.	10. silly

Bonus Box: On the back of this sheet, write a story about Viola Swamp visiting your classroom.

How To Use This Unit

— Read the story *Miss Nelson Is Back* to your children. Encourage them to discuss the events of the story. Display and share other books from the Miss Nelson series listed below. Have students compare and contrast the books and identify their favorite parts.

    Miss Nelson Is Missing! (Houghton Mifflin Company, 1987)
    Miss Nelson Has A Field Day (Houghton Mifflin Company, 1988)

— Your students may also be interested in reading other Harry Allard books, which include the following:

    The Stupids Die (Houghton Mifflin Company, 1981)
    The Stupids Have A Ball (Houghton Mifflin Company, 1984)
    The Stupids Step Out (Houghton Mifflin Company, 1977)
    The Stupids Take Off (Houghton Mifflin Company, 1989)
    Bumps In The Night (Bantam Books, Inc., 1984)

Author Profile
Harry Allard

College professor, translator, and writer: Harry Allard is a success at whatever he does. He has always been interested in languages. Upon meeting author/illustrator James Marshall, Allard was inspired to write children's books. This remarkable team has published such popular titles as the Miss Nelson series, The Stupids series, and *It's So Nice To Have A Wolf Around The House*, among others.

Allard prefers writing books that don't have a message, believing that there is enough time as adults to worry about life's problems. Children should have other things to think about. Allard admits that writing children's books does not allow for the writer to show off his vocabulary, but he enjoys mulling over the words, simplifying his stories to perfection.

Answer Key
Page 61

5
1
6
7
10
4
3
8
9
2

Answer Key
Page 63

1. Miss Nelson
2. Viola Swamp
3. Viola Swamp
4. Mr. Blandsworth
5. Miss Nelson
6. Mr. Blandsworth
7. Viola Swamp
8. Miss Nelson

Answer Key
Page 64

1. Miss Nelson is absent from school.
2. Mr. Blandsworth is the substitute.
3. The children are bored with their substitute.
4. Some children dress up as Miss Nelson.
5. The children have fun around town.
6. Miss Nelson sees the children out of school.
7. Viola Swamp arrives.
8. Miss Nelson is back! (answer given)

Name_____

Who's Who?

Read each description.
Cut and glue the matching picture in each frame.

1	2	3
had tonsils out	frightened children	made children do a lot of work

4	5	6
was fooled by the children	called the school	planned boring activities

Bonus Box: On the back of this sheet, draw a picture of your teacher. Write three things you like best about your teacher.

7	8
found a mask under a desk	saw the class away from school

Miss Nelson   Miss Nelson   Viola Swamp   Mr. Blandsworth

Miss Nelson   Viola Swamp   Viola Swamp   Mr. Blandsworth

Hot On The Trail!

Read the sentences.
Cut out and glue the sentences in the order that they happened.

Beginning

Ending

Miss Nelson is back!

| Viola Swamp arrives. | The children have fun around town. | Mr. Blandsworth is the substitute. | The children are bored with their substitute. | Some children dress up as Miss Nelson. | Miss Nelson is absent from school. | Miss Nelson sees the children out of school. |

Toe-Tappin' Terms

Read each sentence.
Find the meaning of the underlined word or words in the trunk below.
Write the matching letter on the object in front of each sentence.

 1. Grandpa used to dance, sing, and tell jokes on the <u>vaudeville</u> <u>stage</u>.

 2. In the attic there were <u>faded</u> posters of Grandpa.

 3. Grandpa used a <u>shammy</u> to wipe his tap shoes.

 4. To make a stage, Grandpa <u>aimed</u> the lamps like spotlights.

 5. Grandpa <u>glided</u> across the stage.

 6. The <u>echo</u> of Grandpa's voice rang out.

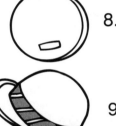 7. Grandpa pulled a <u>hanky</u> from his pocket.

 8. For the grand <u>finale</u>, Grandpa did a tap dance.

 9. He wore a black <u>top hat</u> from the trunk.

 10. As he tapped, his <u>polished</u> tap shoes shined in the light.

a. a sound that repeats itself
b. the last part of a show or song
c. pointed in a certain direction
d. smooth and shiny
e. having very little color or brightness
f. a tall hat worn mostly by men
g. moved smoothly and quietly
h. a soft leather cloth
i. a cloth often used to wipe the nose and face
j. a platform where many kinds of acts are performed

Bonus Box: Pretend you are going to perform in a vaudeville show. Think about what you would wear and what you would do. On the back of this sheet, draw and color yourself performing!

Song And Dance Man
Written by Karen Ackerman & Illustrated by Stephen Gammell

When three lively youngsters come to visit Grandpa, he enchants them with an afternoon of happy, "tappy" vaudeville song and dance. Along with the entertainment, the grandchildren receive a history lesson and a bit of their family legacy. Your students are sure to enjoy this 1989 Caldecott Medal Book!

Extension Activities

— Youngsters are easily entranced by stories of long ago. Solicit tales of days gone by from your students' grandparents or older friends. Invite the volunteers into your classroom to share their tales. Or ask each volunteer to record his or her story of a bygone time with the assistance of his young relative or friend and a cassette tape recorder. If desired, the storyteller may bring a related relic to school or send one along with his tape. These marvelous memories are sure to make lasting impressions on your youngsters. Have students express their appreciation for the special stories by sending hand-decorated thank-you notes to the storytellers.

— Nurture a special bond between your students and their elders throughout the school year by inviting grandparents or other elderly members of the community to help in your classroom. Whether they're listening to students read or helping students practice their math facts, these special visits will be looked forward to by all. And your students will be taking advantage of one of society's most valuable resources—our elderly.

Book Corner
Books About Grandparents

There are numerous books in this special category. Enlist the help of your media specialist in locating the books owned by your school library. Here are a few titles to get you started!

Annie And The Old One • Written by Miska Miles & Illustrated by Peter Parnall • Published by Little, Brown And Company

Grandad Bill's Song • Written by Jane Yolen & Illustrated by Melissa Bay Mathis • Published by Philomel Books

Grandma's House • Written by Elaine Moore & Illustrated by Elise Primavera • Published by Lothrop, Lee & Shepard Books

Grandma's Promise • Written by Elaine Moore & Illustrated by Elise Primavera • Published by Lothrop, Lee & Shepard Books

Grandpa & Bo • Written & Illustrated by Kevin Henkes • Published by Greenwillow Books

Grandpa's Face • Written by Eloise Greenfield & Illustrated by Floyd Cooper • Published by Philomel Books

The Canada Geese Quilt • Written by Natalie Kinsey-Warnock & Illustrated by Leslie W. Bowman • Published by Dutton Children's Books

Thunder Cake • Written & Illustrated by Patricia Polacco • Published by Philomel Books

When I Am Old With You • Written by Angela Johnson & Illustrated by David Soman • Published by Orchard Books

Answer Key

1. j
2. e
3. h
4. c
5. g
6. a
7. i
8. b
9. f
10. d

Name _____

Song-And-Dance Sequencing

Number the events in the order that they happened in the story.
Color Grandpa; then cut on the dotted lines.
Staple the strips to the cutout in order.

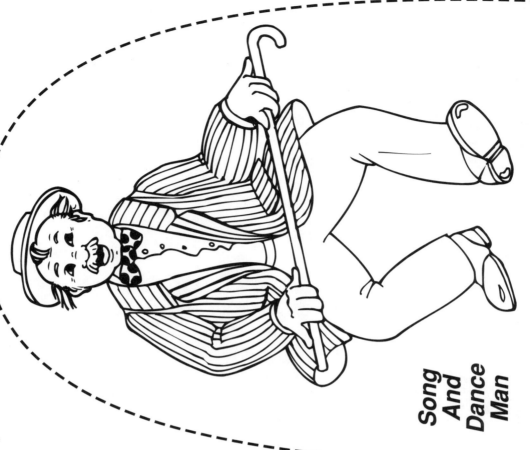

Song
And
Dance
Man

Staple strips here.

©The Education Center, Inc. • *The Best Of Teacher's Helper® Literature • Grades 2–3 • TEC1473*

○ Then Grandpa performs the grand finale.

○ He sprinkles a little powder on the floor.

○ Grandpa polishes his shoes and puts them on.

○ In the attic, Grandpa finds the dusty brown trunk.

○ Next he sings, tells jokes, and does tricks.

○ Grandpa begins to talk about the good old days.

○ Then he slowly closes the door to the attic.

○ Grandpa puts his old-time treasures in the trunk.

○ The trunk is filled with old-time things.

○ Grandpa begins to dance.

67

Follow-up Activity

. For a sturdier final project, have each student glue his completed cutout onto a 6" x 7" piece of colorful tagboard, then trim the tagboard to create an eye-catching border.

Answer Key

1. Grandpa begins to talk about the good old days.
2. In the attic, Grandpa finds the dusty brown trunk.
3. The trunk is filled with old-time things.
4. Grandpa polishes his shoes and puts them on.
5. He sprinkles a little powder on the floor.
6. Grandpa begins to dance.
7. Next he sings, tells jokes, and does tricks.
8. Then Grandpa performs the grand finale.
9. Grandpa puts his old-time treasures in the trunk.
10. Then he slowly closes the door to the attic.

Name _____

In The Spotlight

Complete each sentence.
Use a crayon to outline the large stars.
Color the small stars.

My
favorite
part of the
story was
_____
_____
_____

If
I could
talk to
Grandpa, I
would tell him
_____
_____
_____

I
think
Grandpa
was a great
performer because
_____
_____
_____

He
probably
enjoys
remembering
the good old days because
_____
_____
_____

One
thing I
learned
from the story was
_____
_____
_____
_____

Cut out the stars.
Use the cutouts to make a poster.

How To Use Page 69

Here's the perfect finale to *Song And Dance Man!* Before students complete individual copies of page 69, have each student position a 12" x 18" sheet of yellow construction paper vertically in front of him, then bring together the two top corners and carefully pinch the center mark. Next demonstrate how to cut a large triangle from the paper by cutting from the center pinch mark to each of the lower corners. Instruct each student to glue his resulting triangle atop a 12" x 18" sheet of black construction paper. Next have each youngster label the long pointed end of his triangle "In The Spotlight," then draw and color a picture of the song and dance man from the story in the remainder of the triangle. Set these projects aside until page 69 has been completed.

When students have finished page 69, they can glue their resulting cutouts atop the black paper. Encourage each student to personalize the front of his project and to write the title and author of the book on the back.

Answer Key
Answers will vary.

Name _____

Discovering Stars

Sometimes, people make up stories to help explain things in nature that they don't understand.

The Cheyenne legend *Her Seven Brothers* was created long ago to help explain how the Big Dipper came to be.

Below is the constellation Ursa Major. It is also called "The Great Bear." How do you think the bear became part of the sky? Write your own legend to explain what happened.

_____

_____

_____

_____

_____

_____

_____

_____

_____

_____

_____

_____

_____

Bonus Box: This is the constellation Leo, the Lion. On the back of your paper, draw Leo as you think a storyteller might see it.

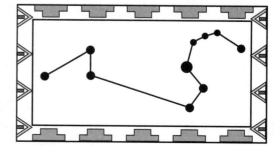

How To Use This Literature Unit (Pages 71–76)

The student activities on pages 71, 73, and 75 are designed to be used in conjunction with the following books by Paul Goble: *Her Seven Brothers, The Gift Of The Sacred Dog,* and *The Girl Who Loved Wild Horses.* If desired, use the information in "Background For The Teacher: Paul Goble" to tell your students something about the author.

How To Use Page 71

See "Setting The Scene" for a prereading activity; then read aloud *Her Seven Brothers* by Paul Goble (Bradbury Press, 1988). Discuss the book with your students before having them complete the activity.

Story Summary
Her Seven Brothers

In this retelling of a Cheyenne legend, the creation of one of the most famous constellations—the Big Dipper—is explained.

Setting The Scene

On the chalkboard draw stars to represent the Big Dipper constellation and ask students to identify it. If the students seem perplexed, connect the stars to reveal the big dipper shape. Tell students that you are going to read aloud a story that tells how the Cheyenne people believe this constellation was created. Before you begin the story, invite students to share their ideas on how the constellation might have been formed.

Background For The Teacher
Paul Goble: 1933–

Paul Goble's interest in the culture and lifestyle of Native Americans began at an early age. As a youngster growing up in England, he had a keen interest in nature and in all aspects of Native Americans. He read book after book, and listened to stories his mother read to him. Paul never lost his fascination with these people whose lives and beliefs were so interwoven with nature.

Paul first visited the United States in 1959 as a student. After spending several summers on Indian reservations and being adopted into the Yakima and Sioux tribes, he moved to the United States in 1977.

One of the original reasons Goble retold Native American myths and legends was to increase the sense of pride that Native American children felt for their culture. Another of his purposes is to preserve bits of the culture for future generations. Each of his books emphasizes the harmonious relationship between man and nature, which has traditionally been an important aspect of Native American life. Building on children's natural curiosity and love of animals, Goble retells legends—hoping that the stories will help children be inspired by nature, as well as be respectful of it.

Follow-Up Activity

Set aside time for students to read their legends to their classmates. Then, if desired, read aloud *The Lost Children* by Paul Goble (Bradbury Press, 1993). In this Blackfoot Indian legend, six neglected orphaned brothers decide to go to the Above World where they become the constellation Pleiades or the "Lost Children."

Is That A Fact?

Color and cut out the fact and opinion buffalo cards.

Place each fact card on a fact statement.
Place each opinion card on an opinion statement.

Put a drop of glue on each •.
Glue the cards in place.

1. • A young boy went to the hills looking for help.

2. • Sacred Dogs were smarter than buffaloes.

3. • The people did not look hard enough for the buffalo herds.

4. • The people were not able to find the buffalo herds.

5. • The white Sacred Dogs were the most beautiful of all.

6. • It was easy for the boy to be brave.

7. • A Sacred Dog could do many things that a dog could do.

8. • The people were excited when they saw the Sacred Dogs.

9. • The Sacred Dogs came in many colors.

10. • The Sacred Dogs would be much happier if they were free.

When you have finished, color the page!

Note To Teacher: For each student, duplicate one set of the Buffalo Cards on page 74.

Materials Needed For Each Student
— pencil
— scissors
— glue
— crayons
— one set of Buffalo Cards (see below)

Story Summary
The Gift Of The Sacred Dog
The Great Spirit, responding to a little boy's prayer for help for his hungry people, sends the gift of the Sacred Dogs—horses—with which the Indian tribe can hunt for buffalo herds.

Buffalo Cards

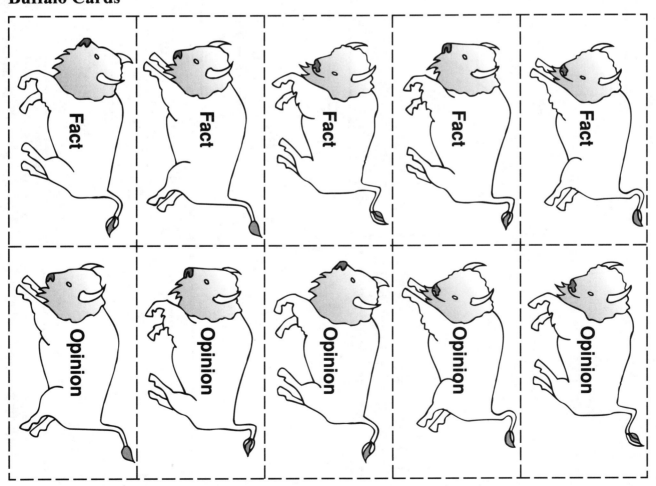

Paul Goble
The Girl Who Loved Wild Horses Vocabulary

The Rocky Trail

Directions for two players:

1. Stack the cards facedown in the box.
2. Place your markers on Start.
3. In turn, draw a card and read the sentence aloud.
4. Say the word that means the same thing as the underlined word. Check the answer key.
5. If correct, flip the coin and move.
   Heads = 1 space
   Tails = 2 spaces
6. The first player to reach Finish wins.

Start

Follow the buffalo. Go ahead one space.

Your horse is tired. Rest for one turn.

You see a flash of lightning. Move ahead one space.

Playing Cards

Ouch! Walked into a cactus! Go back one space.

Finish

Materials Needed For Each Student
— copy of the gameboard on page 75
— 9" x 12" sheet of construction paper
— construction-paper copy of this page
— crayons or markers
— glue
— zippered press-on pocket
— scissors
— coin

Answer Key
1. liked
2. escaped from
3. got on
4. young horse
5. chased
6. well
7. thin
8. dancing
9. snowstorm
10. faraway
11. wandered
12. soft
13. groups
14. disappeared
15. jumped

Directions For The Students
How To Make The Game On Page 75
1. Personalize and color a copy of the gameboard.
2. Glue the gameboard onto a 9" x 12" sheet of construction paper.
3. Attach a zippered press-on pocket to the back of the project.
4. Color each Game Marker differently; then cut them out.
5. Cut out the Game Cards and Answer Key.
6. Store the Game Markers, Game Cards, Answer Key, and coin inside the press-on pocket.

Game Markers

Game Cards

1. The hunters <u>admired</u> the brave horse.	**2.** The stallion <u>dodged</u> the hunters and wasn't caught.	**3.** The hunters <u>mounted</u> their horses and rode off.
hurt / liked	escaped from / fought with	got on / tied up
4. Each year the girl took a <u>colt</u> home to her parents.	**5.** It seemed like the thunder <u>pursued</u> the horses.	**6.** The tired girl slept <u>soundly</u>.
young horse / young buffalo	chased / scared	poorly / well
7. <u>Wispy</u> clouds streaked the sky.	**8.** The horse was <u>prancing</u> around the girl.	**9.** The horses found shelter during the winter <u>blizzard</u>.
thick / thin	eating / dancing	heat wave / snowstorm
10. The <u>distant</u> thunder did not awaken the girl.	**11.** The horses <u>roamed</u> the plains.	**12.** The sound was so <u>faint</u>, the girl did not hear it.
faraway / loud	wandered / slept on	loud / soft
13. The people followed the <u>herds</u> of buffalo.	**14.** The girl <u>vanished</u> and was never seen again.	**15.** The girl <u>leapt</u> onto the horse so it would not get away.
groups / calves	hid / disappeared	jumped / fell

Summing Up Maggie

Think about what has happened in the story.
Write your ideas below.

Chapter(s): 1 2 3 4 5 6 7 8
(Circle the completed chapters.)

Setting

Characters

Summary

What Do You Think?

How would you rate the story so far? (Circle one.)

Explain: _____

Okay   Good   Excellent

How To Use This Literature Unit (Pages 77–82)

The student activities on pages 77, 79, and 81 are designed to accompany *Muggie Maggie,* a beginning chapter book by Beverly Cleary. The book may be read aloud to students, or it may be read independently by students if appropriate. If desired use a prereading activity to introduce the book (see "Setting The Scene").

Story Summary
Muggie Maggie
By Beverly Cleary

Maggie is not getting off to the best start in third grade. On top of everything else that is not going her way, she is far from thrilled about having to learn cursive. In fact, she decides she absolutely won't do it! Will Maggie ever change her mind? This realistic portrayal of a girl caught between pride and practicality will surely have more than a few heads nodding in empathy!

How To Use Page 77

Duplicate for each student three copies of page 77. Then plan to use this open-ended activity at various intervals throughout the story. For example, following chapter 3 have each student identify the chapters that have been read by circling the appropriate numbers on the activity sheet. Have each student list the characters that have been introduced, describe the setting, and summarize the story. Create a writing prompt, or select the one listed below, for students to use in completing the "What Do You Think?" section. Conclude the activity by encouraging students to critique the story.

Chapter:	Writing Prompt:
3	How would you convince Maggie to write cursive if you were her teacher?
6	Why do you think Mrs. Leeper chose Maggie to be the message monitor?
8	If a new student came to class who refused to write cursive, what do you think Maggie might say to him or her?

Background For The Teacher
Beverly Cleary: 1916–

As a child growing up in Oregon amidst two world wars and economic hardships, Beverly Cleary longed to read honest stories of real kids and their true-life experiences. As a children's librarian, Cleary found herself frustrated in her search for interesting, easy-to-read books that would speak to the average, ordinary child. Finally she decided to fill the void by writing her own children's books. Her first book, *Henry Huggins,* was published in 1950. And 45 years later, Henry, Beezus, Ramona, and the many other endearing characters who fill Cleary's books are as popular as ever with both children and adults.

Setting The Scene

Before beginning the story, poll your class to discover how many students are eager to become proficient cursive writers. Encourage students to discuss the pros and cons of writing in cursive. If desired record the youngsters' ideas on a chart and compare with those provided by Maggie, her parents, and her teacher as you progress through the story. Follow up this discussion by reading aloud—or asking students to read—the first chapter in the book. In this chapter, Maggie, after deciding that cursive writing is "dumb," decides she simply won't learn it. Can she be convinced to change her mind?

Crack The Code

For Maggie, reading cursive messages was like cracking a code.

Crack the secret code below to find vocabulary words from the story.

Use the Code Box.

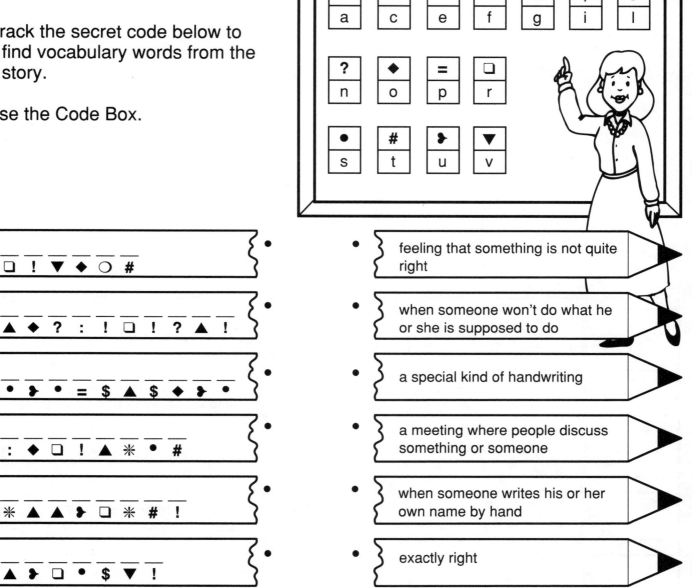

Code Box

✳	▲	!	:	■	$	○
a	c	e	f	g	i	l

?	◆	=	▢
n	o	p	r

●	#	❧	▼
s	t	u	v

▢ ! ▼ ◆ ○ # • • feeling that something is not quite right

▲ ◆ ? : ! ▢ ! ? ▲ ! • • when someone won't do what he or she is supposed to do

● ❧ ● = $ ▲ $ ◆ ❧ ● • • a special kind of handwriting

: ◆ ▢ ! ▲ ✳ ● # • • a meeting where people discuss something or someone

✳ ▲ ▲ ❧ ▢ ✳ # ! • • when someone writes his or her own name by hand

▲ ❧ ▢ ● $ ▼ ! • • exactly right

● $ ■ ? ✳ # ❧ ▢ ! • • to tell about something before it happens

● = ▢ $? ■ $? ■ • • quickly leaping forward

Now draw a line to connect each word with its definition.

Bonus Box: Write a message using a secret code that you create. Give it to a friend to solve.

How To Use Page 79

Use this activity after chapter 5 has been read. After students have decoded the vocabulary words, challenge them to recall how the words were used in the story. Provide assistance as needed. Then have each student complete the matching activity. If desired ask each child to write and illustrate a sentence on another sheet of paper that includes one or more vocabulary words.

Answer Key

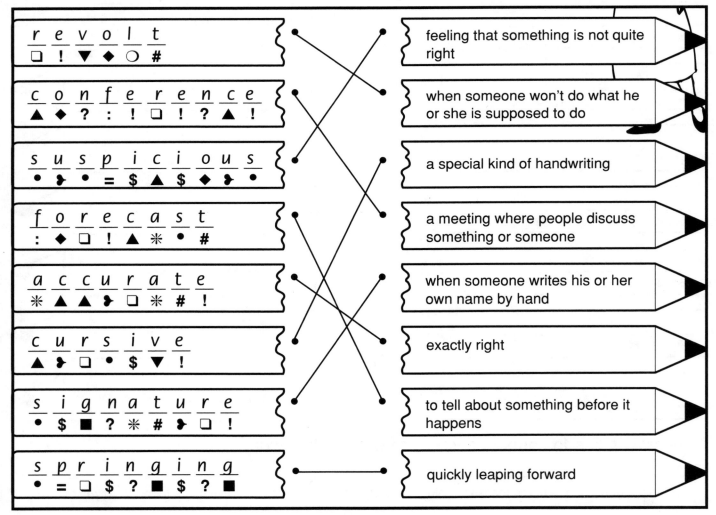

One Thing Leads To Another

Read the sentences.
Use the code to color the circles.

1. ◯ Maggie thought cursive was dumb.
   ◯ Maggie refused to learn cursive.

2. ◯ Maggie's pride kept her from trying to learn cursive.
   ◯ Maggie knew her classmates were watching her.

3. ◯ Maggie spelled her name "M-u-g-g-i-e."
   ◯ Maggie's classmates called her "Muggie Maggie."

4. ◯ Mrs. Madden sent Maggie a pen.
   ◯ Maggie wrote a thank-you note.

5. ◯ Mrs. Leeper chose Maggie to be message monitor.
   ◯ Mrs. Leeper wanted Maggie to read the notes.

6. ◯ Maggie couldn't read Mrs. Leeper's notes.
   ◯ Maggie had not learned cursive.

7. ◯ Maggie started trying to learn cursive.
   ◯ Maggie wanted to read Mrs. Leeper's notes.

8. ◯ Maggie found out that the notes were about her.
   ◯ Maggie was shocked and angry.

Write your own cause and effect sentences about the story.
Use the color code to color the circles.

◯ _____
◯ _____

Bonus Box: Suppose your teacher wrote a note about you and sent it to another teacher. What do you think the note would say? On the back of this paper, write your teacher's note. Write the note in cursive, if you like!

How To Use Page 81

Use this activity at the conclusion of the story. For added practice, have each student read aloud the cause and effect statements that he wrote. Then have each student call upon a classmate to distinguish between the cause and effect statements.

Patterns

Duplicate and cut out a class supply of the note patterns below. Write (in cursive, if appropriate) and deliver a positive note to each student.

Dear _____,

  You are the apple of my eye

because _____

_____

_____

_____

_____

_____

_____

_____ _____

Teacher   Date

©The Education Center, Inc.

Dear _____,

  You are the apple of my eye

because _____

_____

_____

_____

_____

_____

_____

_____ _____

Teacher   Date

©The Education Center, Inc.

Jackson Daily News

Jackson, Wyoming

Day _____   Date _____   25 cents

★ _____ ★

Reported by _____

_____

_____

_____

_____

_____

_____

_____

_____

_____

_____

_____

_____

_____

How To Use This Literature Unit
Pages 83–88

The student activities on pages 83, 85, and 87 are designed to accompany *Stone Fox*—a chapter book by John Reynolds Gardiner.

How To Use Page 83

1. Use this activity after chapter 2 has been read. If desired you may also repeat a similar activity after chapters 4, 5, 6, and 10 (see step 7 for further details).

2. Ask students to recall the events from chapters 1 and 2. Then enlist your students' help in locating Wyoming (the setting of the story) on a map of the United States.

3. Explain that Grandfather's farm is located near the town of Jackson (this is revealed in chapter 3). Then explain that you'd like each student to pretend that he's a newspaper reporter for the local newspaper.

4. Distribute copies of page 83. Guide students in writing the day and date in the provided spaces. Next write the headline "Grandson Harvests Potato Crop" on the chalkboard, and ask each student to copy it on his paper between the stars.

5. Challenge each child to summarize the events from the first two chapters in a newspaper article. Then in the box have each student draw and color a photograph of Willy and Searchlight working the potato field.

6. Set aside time for each journalist to share his work.

7. If desired, have students write additional newspaper articles after the following chapters. Provide students with copies of page 83. Use the provided headlines or create your own:
   — after chapter 4: "Tax Collector Comes To Town"
   — after chapter 5: "Grandson Refuses To Give Up"
   — after chapter 6: "Stone Fox Enters Dogsled Race"
   — after chapter 10: "An Unforgettable Race"

Story Summary
Stone Fox
By John Reynolds Gardiner

Little Willy lives with his grandfather on a potato farm in Wyoming. His grandfather has kept a secret from the boy—ten years of unpaid back taxes that total $500. Grandfather, fearing his farm will be lost, loses his will to live. Determined to not lose his grandfather or his grandfather's farm, ten-year-old Willy devises a plan that includes entering the National Dogsled Race with his faithful dog, Searchlight. The winner of the race earns $500—just enough to pay the back taxes. Even though young Willy must race against Stone Fox, a Shoshone Indian who has never lost a race, his determination never wavers. Leading the race—with only 100 feet to go—Willy's beloved dog has a heart attack and dies. Touched by the boy's will to win, Stone Fox detains the other race contestants so that Willy can carry Searchlight across the finish line and win the race.

Stone Fox is based on a legend the author was told over a cup of coffee in Idaho Falls, Idaho. Though Stone Fox and the other characters are purely fictitious, the tragic ending to the story reportedly happened.

Background For The Teacher
John Reynolds Gardiner: 1944–

When John Reynolds Gardiner talks to students, he makes one thing clear—no one should let a fear of failure stifle his or her desire to write. He also encourages youngsters to read, read, read. As a child Gardiner loved to tell stories and was known for having a great imagination. But getting his ideas down on paper was another matter. A self-described "lousy speller" and a reluctant reader, Gardiner remembers his mother begging him to read. He also recalls being told that he'd never pass college English because his grammar and spelling were so poor. But despite the odds, Gardiner graduated from the University of California in Los Angeles. He attributes his success to his math and science knowledge—the same knowledge that enabled him to become a thermal analyst for aerospace engineering firms. No doubt Gardiner was searching for a creative outlet when he founded a company that invented plastic ties in which guppies could swim. Finally, when Gardiner was 28 years old, his brother dragged him to a writing conference. Gardiner feared rejection—but instead he found inspiration. Six years later he sold his first book, *Stone Fox*. The author has since written other chapter books for children including *Top Secret* and *General Butterfingers*.

Willy And A Way

Color the potatoes. Use the color code.
Explain each answer on the lines.

Color Code
brown = I agree.
yellow = I disagree.

If Grandfather wanted to, he could get well. _____

Doc Smith is a good doctor. _____

Willy is a very responsible boy. _____

Searchlight is smarter than the average dog. _____

It was wise of Willy to spend his college money. _____

Both Willy and Stone Fox want to win the race for good reasons. _____

Willy should be worried about winning the race. _____

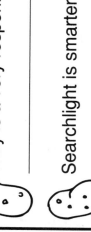

How To Use Page 85

1. Talk with your students about opinions. Lead students to understand that an opinion is based upon a person's judgment, which means that different people will have different opinions. Explain that sometimes people change their opinions, too. This usually happens when a person learns more about a topic.

2. Give each student a copy of page 85 to complete. Be sure that students understand that since opinions can differ, there are no right or wrong answers.

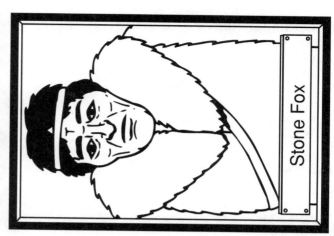

Doc Smith

Stone Fox

Searchlight

Lester

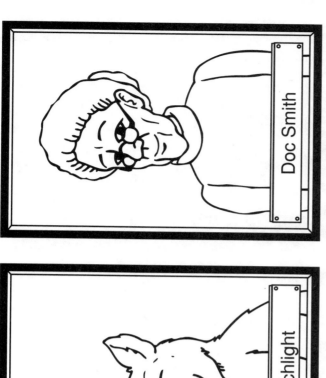

Willy

Mr. Foster

Grandfather

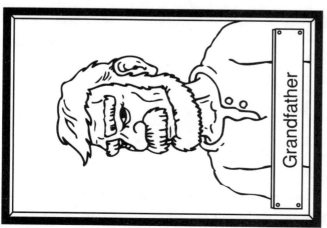

Mr. Snyder

Materials Needed For Each Student

— a copy of page 87
— crayons or markers
— scissors
— eight 3 1/2" x 4 1/2" construction-paper cards
— glue
— eight information cards (see below)
— a letter-size envelope

How To Use Page 87

1. Use this activity at the completion of the book.
2. As a class discuss each of the characters shown on page 87. Provide time for students to color and cut out the character cards.
3. Distribute the construction-paper cards and ask each student to glue each character card onto a different construction-paper card.
4. Distribute the information cards. Have each child complete an information card for each character, then cut it out and glue it to the back of the appropriate construction-paper card.
5. While the completed character cards are drying, have each student write "Stone Fox by John Reynolds Gardiner" on the front of a letter-size envelope. Then have each child write his name on the back before decorating the envelope to his liking.
6. Have students store their character cards inside their decorated envelopes. Encourage students to use the cards to help them retell the story of Stone Fox for their family members and friends.

Willy

Stone Fox
by
John Reynolds Gardiner

Information Cards

_____
(Character Name)

In the story this character _____

_____

_____

What I liked best about this character

was _____

_____

_____

_____
(Character Name)

In the story this character _____

_____

_____

What I liked best about this character

was _____

_____

_____

Name _____

"Kanga-snooze"

Read each word meaning.
Write the word on the line.
Use the Word Bank.

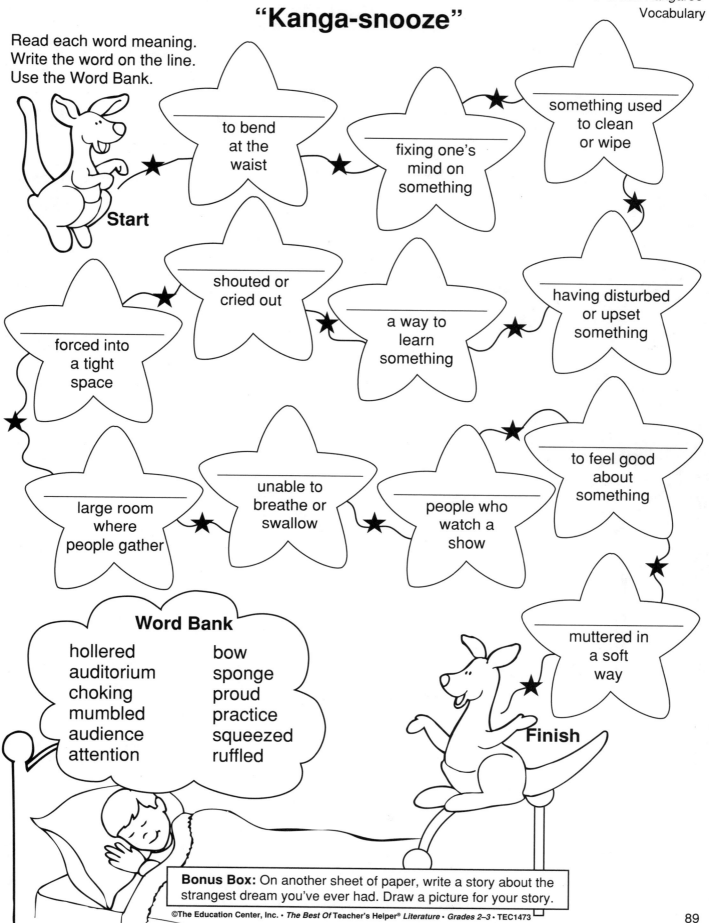

Start

_____ to bend at the waist

_____ fixing one's mind on something

_____ something used to clean or wipe

_____ shouted or cried out

_____ a way to learn something

_____ having disturbed or upset something

_____ forced into a tight space

_____ large room where people gather

_____ unable to breathe or swallow

_____ people who watch a show

_____ to feel good about something

_____ muttered in a soft way

Finish

Word Bank

hollered
auditorium
choking
mumbled
audience
attention

bow
sponge
proud
practice
squeezed
ruffled

Bonus Box: On another sheet of paper, write a story about the strangest dream you've ever had. Draw a picture for your story.

Extension Activity
Self-Concept/Making A Badge

— In the beginning of the story, Freddy felt that he was not special. Being cast in the school play helped him to understand that he was special after all! He could do something that his brother and sister could not.

Provide students with white construction-paper copies of the badge below. Have students draw and color pictures of themselves in the ovals. Then have students write sentences telling what makes them special. (Students might write about something they do especially well at home or at school.) Have students embellish their badges with markers and glitter. Your students are sure to beam with pride as they wear these badges throughout the day!

Badge

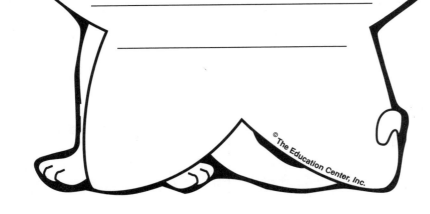

I'm special because _____

_____

_____

© The Education Center, Inc.

90

On Stage With Sequence

Read each sentence below.
Cross out two sentences that don't belong.
Cut and glue the rest of the sentences in the order that they happened in the story.

1.		5.	
2.		6.	
3.		7.	
4.		8.	

Bonus Box: On the back of this sheet, draw a picture of yourself as the Green Kangaroo. Write a story about your part in the play.

- -

Freddy tells his family that he will be the Green Kangaroo.	Freddy dreams about green kangaroos.
The audience laughs at Freddy.	Freddy tells Ms. Gumber he wants to be in the play.
Freddy takes a bow all by himself.	Freddy spills his milk at dinner.
Ms. Matson gives Freddy a part in the play.	Ms. Matson thanks Freddy.
Ms. Gumber helps Freddy put on his costume.	Freddy says hello to the audience.

Answer Key

1. Freddy tells Ms. Gumber he wants to be in the play.
2. Ms. Matson gives Freddy a part in the play.
3. Freddy tells his family that he will be the Green Kangaroo.
4. Freddy dreams about green kangaroos.
5. Freddy says hello to the audience.
6. The audience laughs at Freddy.
7. Ms. Matson thanks Freddy.
8. Freddy takes a bow all by himself.

Name

The Chalkboard Challenge

If the sentence is **true**, color the square **green**.
If the sentence is **false**, color the square **blue**.

Aa Bb Cc Dd Ee Ff Gg Hh Ii Jj Kk Ll Mm Nn Oo Pp Qq Rr Ss Tt Uu Vv Ww Xx Yy Zz

Freddy's neighbors come to the play. ☐	Freddy sees his cousin in the audience. ☐	Freddy shares a room with Mike. ☐	Freddy is in second grade. ☐	Ms. Gumber is in charge of the play. ☐
The fifth-grade girls make Freddy's costume. ☐	Freddy feels funny before the play. ☐	Freddy tells his family about the play at dinner. ☐	Freddy uses a mirror to practice. ☐	Ellen pinches Freddy. ☐
Mike has been in many plays. ☐	Freddy is unhappy at the end. ☐	The play is for fifth and sixth graders. ☐	Freddy is afraid to take a bow. ☐	$\begin{array}{r} 4 \\ +\ 3 \\ \hline 7 \end{array}$

MEETING FOR SCHOOL PLAY 5TH AND 6TH GRADES ONLY

Bonus Box: Rewrite the false sentences to make them true. Use another sheet of paper.

Bookmark

Duplicate these bookmarks on white construction paper for students. Pass out the bookmarks to introduce the book or as rewards for completing the book. Have students color the bookmark. Laminate if desired; then cut along the dotted lines with an X-acto® knife.

Answer Key

green	blue	green	green	blue
blue	green	green	green	blue
blue	blue	green	blue	

Name _____

Do Just What The List Says

Read each direction.
Read the sentences in that group.
Use the color code to color the circles.

1. Trim the fat.
   ○ Decorate the fat.
   ○ Cut off the fat.

2. Dress the chicken.
   ○ Get the chicken ready to cook.
   ○ Put clothes on the chicken.

3. Change the towels.
   ○ Make the towels look different.
   ○ Put up clean towels.

4. Dust the furniture.
   ○ Take dust off the furniture.
   ○ Put dust on the furniture.

5. Put the lights out.
   ○ Take the lights outside.
   ○ Turn off the lights.

6. Draw the drapes.
   ○ Make pictures of the drapes.
   ○ Close the drapes.

7. Measure two cups of rice.
   ○ Fill 2 measuring cups with rice.
   ○ Use a measuring tape to find out how tall 2 cups of rice are.

8. In this box, draw a picture of your favorite thing that Amelia Bedelia did.

How To Use This Unit

Read *Amelia Bedelia* by Peggy Parish to your class. Discuss the unusual ways that Amelia Bedelia follows directions. Then duplicate pages 95, 97, and 99, and challenge your students to reading comprehension activities Amelia Bedelia–style.

Answer Key

1. red
   green
2. green
   red
3. red
   green
4. green
   red
5. red
   green
6. red
   green
7. green
   red
8. Pictures of Amelia Bedelia will vary.

Name _____

Who Said It?

Read each sentence.
Decide if Amelia Bedelia or Mrs. Rogers said the sentence.
Write the correct name on the line.

1. "I'm not much of a hand at drawing…." _____

2. "But I made a list for you." _____

3. "These folks do want me to do funny things." _____

4. "I think I'll make a surprise for them." _____

5. "Those towels are very nice. Why change them?" _____

6. "Oh, my best towels." _____

7. "I do make good pies." _____

8. "I asked you to draw the drapes." _____

9. "Amelia Bedelia, the sun will fade the furniture." _____

10. "Now I must dress the chicken." _____

11. "…your first day of work. And I can't be here." _____

12. "You do just what the list says." _____

13. "These must be rich folks." _____

14. "Well, look at that. A special powder to dust with!" _____

Bonus Box: On the back of this sheet, write a story about Amelia Bedelia. Give her a new kind of job. Tell about the funny things she does at work.

Answer Key

1. Amelia Bedelia
2. Mrs. Rogers
3. Amelia Bedelia
4. Amelia Bedelia
5. Amelia Bedelia
6. Mrs. Rogers
7. Amelia Bedelia
8. Mrs. Rogers
9. Mrs. Rogers
10. Amelia Bedelia
11. Mrs. Rogers
12. Mrs. Rogers
13. Amelia Bedelia
14. Amelia Bedelia

Funny Amelia!

Here are some new chores for Amelia Bedelia.
In each box, draw what Amelia Bedelia might do for that chore.

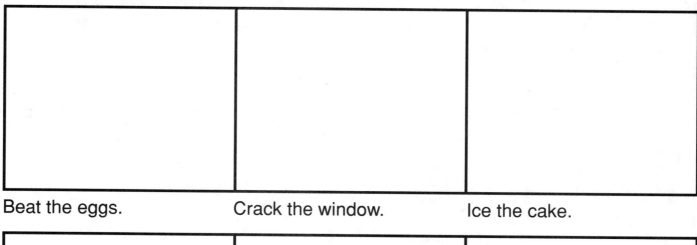

Beat the eggs.	Crack the window.	Ice the cake.

Press the clothes.	Toss the salad.	Throw out the trash.

Here is a list of directions for you.
Look at the pictures above.
Follow each direction.

1. If Amelia Bedelia made a mess, draw a red circle around the picture.

2. If she made something funny, draw stars around the picture.

3. If she did something indoors, put a blue ● above the picture.

Bonus Box: On the back of this sheet, draw pictures of words with different meanings. Here are some words to get you started: *ring, cross, box.*

Have A "Swine" Time Reading!

Present this pass and spend the next 15 minutes reading

_____.

Look What I'm Reading!

I Pig Out On Books!

Look Who Has An Appetite For Books!

This award certifies that

_____
student

read _____

_____

Three Oinks For You!

_____
teacher

_____
date

Name _____

Character Conversation

Cut out the character faces.
Glue each face in front of the sentence that the character said.

1. ☐ "Let's fight for freedom!"

2. ☐ "Let's sail away instead."

3. ☐ "I'll be the ship's captain!"

4. ☐ "Let's blaze our way to the island and show him we mean business!"

5. ☐ "Here we can all *feel* like kings."

6. ☐ "Surrender, you pirate!"

7. ☐ "Don't hurt me!"

8. ☐ "Because I was afraid of you!"

9. ☐ "I've been so lonely here, but I decided it was better to be alone than to be afraid."

10. ☐ "If only we'd talked to each other."

©The Education Center, Inc. • *The Best Of* Teacher's Helper® *Literature* • *Grades 2–3* • TEC1473

 Bouncer Bouncer Bouncer Bouncer Jenny Jenny Jenny Skog Skog Skog

How To Use Pages 101, 103, And 105

Read the story *The Island Of The Skog* by Steven Kellogg aloud to your students. Direct students' attention to the main characters in the story. Then discuss the events of the story with your children. Duplicate pages 101, 103, and 105 for each of your students. Have children complete their pages to demonstrate their comprehension skills. After completing this unit, share other Steven Kellogg books with your students such as:

— *Best Friends* (Dial Books For Young Readers, 1986)
— *Can I Keep Him?* (Dial Books For Young Readers, 1985)
— *The Mysterious Tadpole* (Dial Books For Young Readers, 1977)
— *Pinkerton, Behave!* (Dial Books For Young Readers, 1979)
— *A Rose For Pinkerton* (Dial Books For Young Readers, 1981)

Answer Key

1. Bouncer
2. Jenny
3. Bouncer
4. Bouncer
5. Jenny
6. Bouncer
7. Skog
8. Skog
9. Skog
10. Jenny

Name _____

Here's How It Happened

Blacken the correct circle.

1. Jenny had a party because
   ○ it was her birthday.   ○ it was National Rodent Day.

2. The mice were shaking because
   ○ they had just escaped from the cat.   ○ they were almost caught by
                                               the delivery boy.

3. The mice sailed away to a peaceful island because
   ○ they wanted to feel safe.   ○ they wanted to take a vacation.

4. The mice became very cold on the ship because
   ○ they were running out of food.   ○ winter weather set in.

5. The mice huddled around a waffle iron because
   ○ they were hungry for breakfast.   ○ they were very cold.

6. The mice did somersaults on the beach because
   ○ they wanted to get some exercise.   ○ they were happy to be on land
                                               again.

7. The mice tried to get rid of the Skog because
   ○ they were afraid of him.   ○ there wasn't enough room on the
                                               island for all of them.

8. The mice made a big trap because
   ○ they were trying to hunt for food.   ○ they wanted to catch the Skog.

9. The mice were marooned on the island because
   ○ the Skog cut the ship's rope.   ○ the ship sank.

10. The Skog tried to scare the mice into leaving the island because
    ○ he was afraid of the mice.   ○ he liked living alone.

Bonus Box: How do you think the Skog came to
live on the island? On the back of this sheet, write
a story about the adventures of the Skog's life
and how it arrived on the island. Draw a picture to
illustrate a part of your story.

Answer Key

1. Jenny had a party because
   ○ it was her birthday.   ● it was National Rodent Day.

2. The mice were shaking because
   ● they had just escaped from the cat.   ○ they were almost caught by the delivery boy.

3. The mice sailed away to a peaceful island because
   ● they wanted to feel safe.   ○ they wanted to take a vacation.

4. The mice became very cold on the ship because
   ○ they were running out of food.   ● winter weather set in.

5. The mice huddled around a waffle iron because
   ○ they were hungry for breakfast.   ● they were very cold.

6. The mice did somersaults on the beach because
   ○ they wanted to get some exercise.   ● they were happy to be on land again.

7. The mice tried to get rid of the Skog because
   ● they were afraid of him.   ○ there wasn't enough room on the island for all of them.

8. The mice made a big trap because
   ○ they were trying to hunt for food.   ● they wanted to catch the Skog.

9. The mice were marooned on the island because
   ● the Skog cut the ship's rope.   ○ the ship sank.

10. The Skog tried to scare the mice into leaving the island because
    ● he was afraid of the mice.   ○ he liked living alone.

Read each question.
Write your answer on the lines.

Sound Advice For Skog And Mice

1. The mice were unprepared for winter weather. What would you do to prepare for a cold voyage at sea? _____ _____ _____

2. What do you think the mice expected to find on the island? _____ _____ _____ _____

3. In the story, Jenny said that "[*feeling* like a king] is the most important part of being king...." What do you think she meant by that? _____ _____ _____

4. Why do you think the mice and the Skog were afraid of each other? _____ _____ _____

5. What lessons do you think the mice and the Skog learned from this experience? _____ _____ _____

6. What lessons about making friends have you learned from this story? _____ _____ _____

Bonus Box: What kind of homes do you think the mice made for themselves on the island? Draw a picture of one of their homes on the back of this sheet.

Answer Key

Answers will vary.

In Search Of A Queen

Color each small box a different color.
Then for each sentence:
   Find the meaning of the underlined word in a flower.
   Color the flower to match the box.

☐ 1. Mufaro felt both of his daughters were beautiful and <u>worthy.</u>

☐ 2. Mufaro did not know that Manyara <u>teased</u> her sister.

☐ 3. Nyasha <u>tended</u> her gardens.

☐ 4. Manyara <u>ignored</u> the old woman's advice.

☐ 5. The <u>grove</u> of trees seemed to laugh at Manyara.

☐ 6. In the morning there was <u>commotion</u> in the village.

☐ 7. When Nyasha first saw the city, she stood <u>transfixed.</u>

☐ 8. Nyasha bravely entered the <u>chamber.</u>

☐ 9. The wedding <u>garments</u> were made from the finest cloth.

☐ 10. Nyasha helped prepare a <u>feast</u> for the wedding.

confusion

made fun of

didn't pay attention to

fancy meal

group

took care of

clothes

kind and honest

room

unable to move

Bonus Box: Nyasha grew millet, sunflowers, yams, and vegetables in her garden. On the back of this paper, draw and color what you think Nyasha's garden looked like.

How To Use This Literature Unit (Pages 107–114)

Obtain one or more copies of John Steptoe's book *Mufaro's Beautiful Daughters*. If desired, use a prereading activity to introduce the book (see "Setting The Scene"). Read the book aloud to your students; then lead the youngsters in completing the student activities on pages 107, 109, 111, and 113.

Story Summary
Mufaro's Beautiful Daughters
An African Tale By John Steptoe

At the conclusion of this Caldecott Honor book, students can confirm that there's more to beauty than meets the eye. When the king decides to take a wife, he invites Mufaro's two equally attractive daughters to appear before him. Mufaro happily agrees and declares that only a king could choose between such pretty girls. What Mufaro doesn't realize is that his two beautiful daughters have very different personalities. Steptoe's stunning illustrations of the flora, fauna, and cultural artifacts of Zimbabwe add to the appeal of this inspiring tale.

Background For The Teacher
John Steptoe: 1950–1989

John Steptoe authored and illustrated many award-winning books during his short lifetime. As a child, Steptoe was considered peculiar. His preference to stay inside to paint and draw seemed odd for a boy growing up in a flashy Brooklyn neighborhood filled with slick talk, slick clothes, and slick cars. He attended the High School of Art and Design until his senior year, when he was recruited into a summer program for minority artists. Steptoe's remarkable talent did not go unnoticed. At the end of the program, an art instructor offered Steptoe an apartment over his horse stables. At the young age of 16 and in a place all his own, Steptoe created *Stevie*. He was 19 when the book was published. The first of its kind in American book publishing, *Stevie* was written to and for Black children.

Steptoe's inspiration was nurtured by every child's need for good literature, and he was dedicated to writing for and about Black youngsters. His books were also avenues for self-healing and personal growth. To Steptoe the creative process was equal in importance to the completed project. Sadly, at the young age of 38, Steptoe died of complications from acquired immune deficiency syndrome. Other titles published by this talented author and illustrator include *Baby Says, Birthday, Daddy Is A Monster...Sometimes,* and *The Story Of Jumping Mouse.*

Setting The Scene

A green sock, a little bit of stuffing, a safety pin, craft glue, and two wiggle eyes are all the enticement you'll need to build interest in this read-aloud. Right before your students' eyes, transform the materials into a stuffed snake. (Secure the stuffing inside the sock by pinning closed the opening; then attach the eyes with glue.) Introduce the snake as a character from the story. Be sure to remind your listeners how sneaky snakes can be! Sssssssssssss!

Answer Key
1. kind and honest
2. made fun of
3. took care of
4. didn't pay attention to
5. group
6. confusion
7. unable to move
8. room
9. clothes
10. fancy meal

Nyoka

- wise
- boastful
- generous
- magical
- clever
- creative

I think the word that best describes Nyoka is ___

because ___

I think the word that least describes Nyoka is ___

because ___

Nyasha

- brave
- kind
- worthy
- weak
- beautiful
- thankful

I think the word that best describes Nyasha is ___

because ___

I think the word that least describes Nyasha is ___

because ___

Mufaro

- proud
- strong
- selfish
- trusting
- happy
- loving

I think the word that best describes Mufaro is ___

because ___

I think the word that least describes Mufaro is ___

because ___

Manyara

- clever
- beautiful
- greedy
- lazy
- worthy
- jealous

I think the word that best describes Manyara is ___

because ___

I think the word that least describes Manyara is ___

because ___

Materials Needed For Each Student

—pencil
—scissors
—glue
—crayons
—4 1/2" x 36" strip of green paper
—construction-paper scraps

How To Use Page 109
Snake Booklet

1. Duplicate student copies of page 109.
2. Instruct students to read the descriptive words below each character's name and complete the two corresponding sentences.
3. Have students color the illustrations, cut on the dotted lines, and set the resulting booklet pages aside until they are needed in the booklet-making process.
4. To make a booklet, fold the green paper strip in half and trim to round the ends of the paper.
5. Unfold the paper and locate the center crease.
6. Glue two booklet pages to the left of the crease and two to the right, leaving the rounded ends blank. (See the illustration.)
7. Use crayons and construction-paper scraps to add facial features to both sides of one rounded end.
8. Working from the decorated end, accordion-fold the project.
9. Partially unfold the project and display it as desired.

Step 6

Completed Project

A Royal Retelling

Cut out and glue the story events in order.

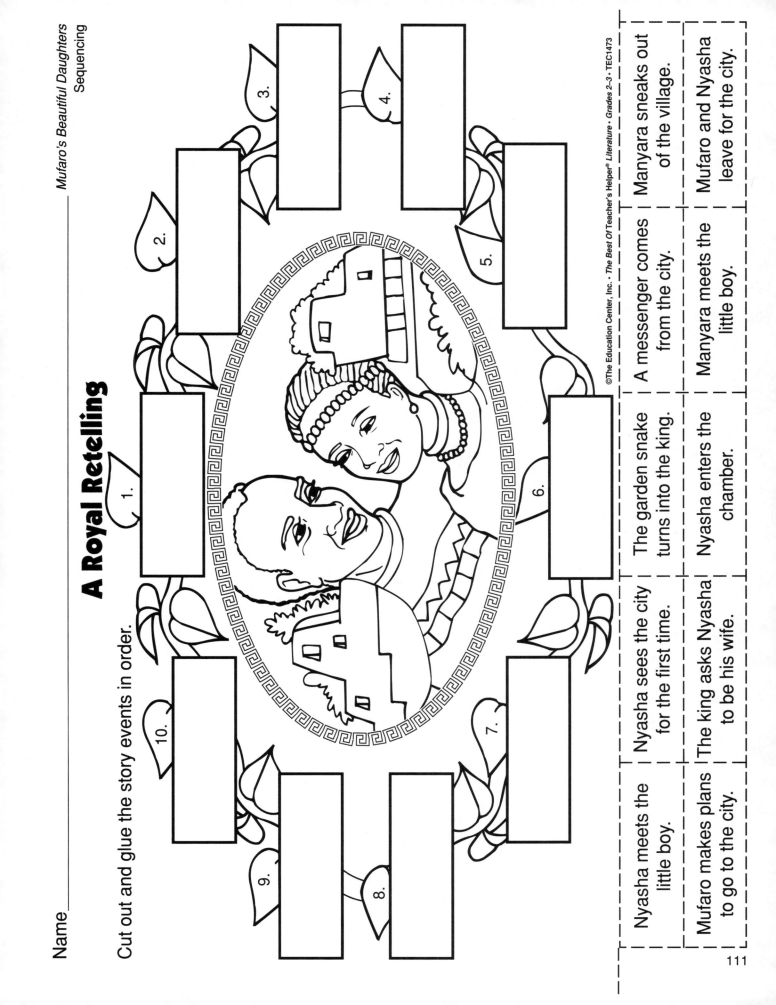

1.

2.

3.

4.

5.

6.

7.

8.

9.

10.

©The Education Center, Inc. • *The Best Of Teacher's Helper® Literature* • Grades 2–3 • TEC1473

Manyara sneaks out of the village.	Mufaro and Nyasha leave for the city.
A messenger comes from the city.	Manyara meets the little boy.
The garden snake turns into the king.	Nyasha enters the chamber.
Nyasha sees the city for the first time.	The king asks Nyasha to be his wife.
Nyasha meets the little boy.	Mufaro makes plans to go to the city.

Answer Key

1. A messenger comes from the city.
2. Mufaro makes plans to go to the city.
3. Manyara sneaks out of the village.
4. Manyara meets the little boy.
5. Mufaro and Nyasha leave for the city.
6. Nyasha meets the little boy.
7. Nyasha sees the city for the first time.
8. Nyasha enters the chamber.
9. The garden snake turns into the king.
10. The king asks Nyasha to be his wife.

Name _____

An African Folktale

Think about the story.
Answer each question.

Why do you think...

Manyara was such an unhappy person?	Nyasha found it so easy to be nice?	Manyara felt kindness was a weakness?
Nyasha ignored her sister's unkind words?	the king disguised himself as a snake?	Nyasha wasn't afraid to enter the chamber?
Manyara became a royal servant?	the author wrote this story?	**Bonus Box:** Use the code to color the stars at the top of the page. **Color Code** one star = an OK story two stars = a good story three stars = a great story four stars = a superb story

How To Use Page 113

Ask students to complete the activity independently; then set aside time for the youngsters to share and discuss their answers. Be sure to emphasize that the questions on the activity were designed to encourage a variety of responses. By carefully listening to their classmates' answers and explanations, the students are sure to gain a greater understanding of the story and at the same time broaden their thinking skills.

Answer Key
Answers will vary.

Chocolate Surprises

Read each sentence.
On the lines explain why you agree
or disagree with the sentence.

Mary is a model student.

_____
_____
_____
_____

Marvin brags too much.

_____
_____
_____
_____

Mrs. Bird is a good teacher.

_____
_____
_____
_____

All children are curious.

_____
_____
_____
_____

Label a wrapper for each bar of candy. Use the code.
Color and cut out the wrappers.
Put a drop of glue on each •.
Glue the wrappers in place.

You Bet!

Candy Wrapper Code:
You Bet! = I agree with the
sentence.
No Way! = I do not agree with the
sentence.

**Candy
Wrappers**

How To Use This Literature Unit
Pages 115–120

The student activities on pages 115, 117, and 119 are designed to accompany *Mary Marony And The Chocolate Surprise,* a beginning chapter book by Suzy Kline (G. P. Putnam's Sons, 1995). The book may be read aloud to students or it may be read independently if appropriate. The book makes a perfect follow-up to an oral reading of Roald Dahl's *Charlie And The Chocolate Factory.*

Story Summary
Mary Marony And The Chocolate Surprise
By Suzy Kline

In this chocolatey romp, second-grader Mary Marony is full of surprises! Exasperated with the mean and inconsiderate ways of her classmate Marvin Higgins, Mary takes matters into her own hands. What unfolds is a sequence of events that takes everyone—even Mary—by surprise.

Students can enjoy more antics of this true-to-life second grader in *Mary Marony, Mummy Girl; Mary Marony Hides Out;* and *Mary Marony And The Snake.*

How To Use Page 115

Use this activity after chapter 4 has been read. When the students have completed the activity, invite them to share their opinions about the sentences that were presented. If time permits, provide additional story-related opinions for the students to consider, or supply school-related opinions for the students to discuss.

Additional Story-Related Opinions:
Audrey is good in math.
Mary is very observant.
Marvin is lucky.
Marvin turned Mrs. Bird's hair gray.
Mary will feel bad about what she's done.

A Terrible Feeling

Color the circle beside the best ending for each sentence.

1. Mary isn't eager to open her candy bar because
   ○ everyone is watching.
   ○ she knows what she has done is wrong.

2. Mary switches candy bars with Elizabeth because
   ○ Mary no longer wants a golden ticket.
   ○ Mary feels she doesn't deserve a golden ticket.

3. Mary wants to tell the truth because
   ○ she knows it is the right thing to do.
   ○ she's afraid Marvin will find out and tell on her.

4. Mary and Elizabeth are good friends because
   ○ Elizabeth does everything Mary asks her to do.
   ○ they like each other.

5. Elizabeth suddenly feels better because
   ○ she ate some crackers and drank some ginger ale.
   ○ she knows she doesn't have a gross disease.

6. Cheating is like lying because
   ○ both are dishonest.
   ○ only bad people cheat and tell lies.

7. Mary doesn't tell her mother about the candy bar incident because
   ○ she is afraid her mother wouldn't understand.
   ○ she doesn't want to spoil her mother's celebration.

8. Mary feels brave when her mother kisses her forehead because
   ○ the kisses remind Mary how much her mother loves her.
   ○ three kisses are a sign of good luck.

9. Mary may stutter more when she is upset because
   ○ it is hard for many people to talk when they are upset.
   ○ she doesn't try hard enough.

10. Mary is afraid to tell the truth because
    ○ she knows she'll get in trouble.
    ○ she knows she will disappoint her friends and her teacher.

Bonus Box: On the back of this sheet, write a note to Mary. Give her advice about telling the truth.

How To Use Page 117

Use this activity after chapter 6 has been read.

Answer Key

1. she knows what she has done is wrong.
2. Mary feels she doesn't deserve a golden ticket.
3. she knows it is the right thing to do.
4. they like each other.
5. she knows she doesn't have a gross disease.
6. both are dishonest.
7. she doesn't want to spoil her mother's celebration.
8. the kisses remind Mary how much her mother loves her.
9. it is hard for many people to talk when they are upset.
10. she knows she will disappoint her friends and her teacher.

Name _____

The Whole Truth

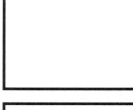

In the end, the whole truth about the golden tickets is learned.
Cut out the story events.
Glue them in order to show what really happens.

1. [ ]   2. [ ]   3. [ ]

10. [ ]      4. [ ]

9. [ ]   5. [ ]

8. [ ]   7. [ ]   6. [ ]

©The Education Center, Inc. • *The Best Of* Teacher's Helper® *Literature* • *Grades 2–3* • TEC1473

| Marvin switches candy bars with Mary. | Mary eats pizza with her teacher. | Mary peeks at her candy bar. | Mary switches candy bars with Marvin. | Marvin peeks at his candy bar. |
| Mary peeks at Marvin's candy bar. | Marvin writes an apology poem for Mary. | Marvin peeks at Mary's candy bar. | Mary tells the truth. | Mary switches candy bars with Elizabeth. |

How To Use Page 119

Use this activity at the conclusion of the story.

Answer Key

1. Marvin peeks at his candy bar.
2. Marvin peeks at Mary's candy bar.
3. Marvin switches candy bars with Mary.
4. Mary peeks at her candy bar.
5. Mary peeks at Marvin's candy bar.
6. Mary switches candy bars with Marvin.
7. Mary switches candy bars with Elizabeth.
8. Mary tells the truth.
9. Marvin writes an apology poem for Mary.
10. Mary eats pizza with her teacher.

Name _____

A Thunder Cake Day

Color Code
In the story,
it happened first = blue
it happened second = purple
it didn't happen = black

Read the sentences in each group.
Use the code to color the raindrops.

1. ○ Grandma shoos the little girl from under the bed.
   ○ The little girl hears thunder.
   ○ The little girl begins to cry.

2. ○ Grandma finds the recipe for Thunder Cake.
   ○ Grandma explains how to count raindrops.
   ○ The little girl and her grandma gather eggs.

3. ○ Grandma picks tomatoes.
   ○ Old Kick Cow gets milked.
   ○ The little girl gathers supplies from the dry shed.

4. ○ The Thunder Cake goes into the oven.
   ○ Grandma tells the little girl how brave she is.
   ○ Grandma clears the table.

5. ○ The little girl is too afraid to eat.
   ○ Cake and tea are served.
   ○ The storm arrives.

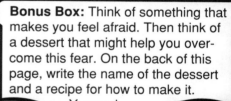

Bonus Box: Think of something that makes you feel afraid. Then think of a dessert that might help you overcome this fear. On the back of this page, write the name of the dessert and a recipe for how to make it. Yummy!

Write your own sentences about the story.
Use the code to color the raindrops.

 _____

○ _____

 _____

How To Use This Literature Unit
Pages 121–126

The student activities on pages 121, 123, and 125 are designed to be used in conjunction with the following books by Patricia Polacco: *Thunder Cake, My Rotten Redheaded Older Brother,* and *Chicken Sunday.* If desired, use the information in "Background For The Teacher" to tell your students something about the author.

How To Use Page 121

Read aloud *Thunder Cake* by Patricia Polacco (Philomel Books, 1990). Discuss the book with your students before having them complete the activity.

Story Summary

Thunder Cake is Patricia Polacco's story about the way her grandmother taught her to face and overcome her fear of thunder.

Background For The Teacher
Patricia Polacco: 1944–

Forty-some years ago, Patricia Polacco's grandmother strolled around an enormous rock in her front yard. "Do you want to know how this got here?" she asked. Patricia looked at the rock and said, "Well, Bubee, that's a rock." Her grandmother replied, "Well, if a rock is all you can see, what a pity!" During the conversation that ensued, Patricia's grandmother told her the story of a falling star. Years later that same story was the inspiration for *Meteor!,* Patricia's first book.

Even though her grandmother died before Patricia's fifth birthday, her storytelling (and that of other family members, including her dad) had a profound effect on Patricia. Much of Patricia's writing is based on experiences she had on her grandmother's farm in Union City, Michigan. After her grandmother's death, Patricia and her family moved to Oakland, California, to a neighborhood characterized by a mix of cultures, races, and religions. It was there that she met her lifelong friend Stewart Washington. *Chicken Sunday* is Patricia's book about Stewart's family.

In Patricia's family, when a child was about to read, it was customary to put a drop of honey on the cover of the book. The message that this symbolized was that, like honey, knowledge is sweet. Like the bee from which the honey came, knowledge may be elusive. But if you chase it through the pages of books, it will finally be yours. For Patricia, the chase was an especially difficult one, since she had undiagnosed learning disabilities. When she was 14, a teacher discovered this well-guarded secret and paid for Patricia to have twice-weekly sessions with a reading specialist.

Years later, Patricia's high school English teacher ridiculed her spelling, but admitted, "...you *do* tell a good story!" The overwhelming majority of people who have read her books can't testify as to her poor spelling, but most wholeheartedly agree that she definitely tells a good story!

Answer Key

1. purple
   blue
   black

2. blue
   black
   purple

3. black
   blue
   purple

4. blue
   purple
   black

5. black
   purple
   blue

What A Pair!

Read each descriptive phrase below.
Decide whom it best describes.
Copy the phrase in that character's box.
If the phrase describes both characters,
copy it in both boxes.

Patricia

Richard

Descriptive Phrases

wishes on a star
runs the fastest
is four years older
passes out
wears glasses
is competitive

learns a lesson about wishes
burps the loudest
has a wonderful Bubbie
drives his sister crazy
is teased by her brother
falls off the merry-go-round

gets stitches
is four years younger
gets the dirtiest
has bright orange hair
has a silly smile
gets sick on rhubarb

How To Use Page 123

Read aloud *My Rotten Redheaded Older Brother* by Patricia Polacco (Simon & Schuster Books For Young Readers, 1994). Discuss the book with your students before having them complete the activity.

Story Summary

Who needs an older brother who can do everything you do, better? Especially an extrarotten, greeny-toothed brother with bright orange hair and glasses! But when Patricia wishes on a shooting star that she can do something—*anything*—to show her brother up, she finds out what wishes—and rotten redheaded older brothers—can really do. This warmhearted tale of comic one-upmanship and brotherly love is sure to be adored by your youngsters.

Answer Key
(The order of the answers in each column will vary.)

Patricia	Richard
wishes on a star	runs the fastest
passes out	is four years older
is competitive	wears glasses
learns a lesson about wishes	is competitive
has a wonderful Bubbie	burps the loudest
is teased by her brother	has a wonderful Bubbie
falls off the merry-go-round	drives his sister crazy
gets stitches	gets the dirtiest
is four years younger	has bright orange hair
gets sick on rhubarb	has a silly smile

A Sunday Surprise

Complete each sentence about the story.
Color.

Cut on the dotted lines.
Staple the pages to the cutout in order.

1.

2. This story was about
_____
_____
_____
_____
_____

3. My favorite part was
_____
_____
_____
_____
_____

4. I think the best char-
acter was _____
_____
because _____
_____
_____

5. This story made me
feel _____
because _____
_____
_____
_____

6. I'd like to tell the
author _____
_____
_____
_____
_____

Chicken Sunday

Staple pages here.

125

Materials Needed For Each Student

— white construction-paper copy of page 125
— pencil
— crayons or markers
— scissors
— access to a stapler

How To Use Page 125

Read aloud *Chicken Sunday* by Patricia Polacco (Philomel Books, 1992). Discuss the book with your students before having them complete the activity.

Story Summary

In this Easter story, Patricia introduces her readers to an African-American family she befriended when she and her mom moved to Oakland, California. The family included Eula Mae Walker and her grandsons, Stewart and Winston Washington. To this day, Patricia claims Stewart as her best friend.

It's just a few days before Easter, and Patricia, Stewart, and Winston are determined to buy Miss Eula the beautiful Easter bonnet she's been admiring. The money the youngsters have saved just isn't enough, so they devise a plan to earn some extra cash. What unfolds is a moneymaking endeavor that evolves from an unselfish act of kindness.

Name _____

Too Much Temptation

Color the picture.
Cut on the dotted lines.
Arrange the events in order.

Glue one end of your colored paper here.

Father discovers the pudding is missing.	Julian puts his finger in the pudding.
Huey puts his finger in the pudding.	Mother comes home.
Mother tastes the pudding.	Father takes a nap.
Father cooks the pudding.	Huey beats the egg yokes.
Julian whips the egg whites.	Father finds the boys under the bed.
The brothers hide under the bed.	The brothers eat spoonfuls of pudding.
Father cuts five lemons in half.	Father cleans up his mess.

To finish the project:
1. Glue one end of your colored paper to the picture cutout.
2. Glue the events on the colored paper in order.
3. Write your name at the bottom of the project.

Bonus Box: On another sheet of paper, draw and color your favorite dessert. Think about how the dessert tastes, how it feels on your tongue, how it smells, and how it looks. Write two descriptive sentences about your favorite dessert.

How To Use This Literature Unit
Pages 127-132

The student activities on pages 127, 129, and 131 are designed to accompany *The Stories Julian Tells* (Random House, Inc.; 1981)—a beginning chapter book by Ann Cameron.

How To Use Page 127

Use this activity after "The Pudding Like A Night On The Sea" has been read.

Materials Needed For Each Student

— a white construction-paper copy of page 127
— markers or crayons
— scissors
— glue
— a 4 1/2" x 12" strip of yellow construction paper

Story Summary
The Stories Julian Tells By Ann Cameron

Julian has a wonderful imagination and he loves to tell stories—especially to his younger brother, Huey, who will believe just about anything. But more often than not, Julian's passion for telling stories lands the twosome in a pack of trouble.

Setting The Scene

Poll your class to find out how many students remember a time when they ended up in trouble because of a story they had told. Invite students to share the lessons these experiences taught them. Tell the youngsters that they'll be reading about a youngster who often finds himself in a pack of trouble because of the stories he tells.

Background For The Teacher
Ann Cameron: 1943–

Ann Cameron was born and raised in Rice Lake, Wisconsin. As a youngster she loved books about characters who struggled to make a happy life for themselves, and who succeeded. She also discovered early on that writing stories was a way to make life the way she thought that it should be. Perhaps this is why Ann knew at a young age (about third grade) that she wanted to be a writer! After high school, Ann studied poetry at Radcliffe College and graduated in 1961 with honors. For two and a half years, she worked in publishing in New York City. Then she attended the University of Iowa Writers' Workshop and in 1972 earned a master's degree in English from the university.

Ann Cameron's debut as a children's book writer came in 1975 when *The Seed*—a story written from a seed's point of view as it emerges from darkness into light—was published. Ann introduced Julian—her imaginative storyteller—in 1981 with *The Stories Julian Tells*. Julian has since appeared in three more books: *More Stories Julian Tells, Julian's Glorious Summer,* and *Julian, Secret Agent.* Most recently, Julian's brother, Huey, took center stage in *The Stories Huey Tells.*

Ann Cameron divides her time between New York City and Penajachel, Guatemala. She lives with two noisy cats, Jane and Special, who—according to her publisher—"often go out dancing on the neighbors' tin roofs in Guatemala." Perhaps the two felines are hoping to appear in Ann's next book!

Answer Key

| Father cuts five lemons in half. |
| Father cooks the pudding. |
| Father cleans up his mess. |
| Father takes a nap. |
| Huey puts his finger in the pudding. |
| Julian puts his finger in the pudding. |
| The brothers eat spoonfuls of pudding. |
| The brothers hide under the bed. |
| Mother comes home. |
| Father discovers the pudding is missing. |
| Father finds the boys under the bed. |
| Huey beats the egg yokes. |
| Julian whips the egg whites. |
| Mother tastes the pudding. |

Justin

Name _____

Catalog Cats

Decide which character or characters from the story each phrase describes.

Write the names on the lines and use the code to color the cats.

If a phrase describes more than one character, color the matching cat more than one color!

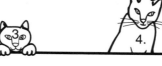

Color Code		
Father	=	black
Julian	=	yellow
Huey	=	brown

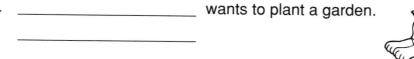

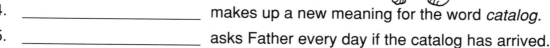

1. _____ wants to plant a garden.

_____

_____

2. _____ knows what a catalog really is.

_____

3. _____ orders a catalog.

4. _____ makes up a new meaning for the word *catalog.*

5. _____ asks Father every day if the catalog has arrived.

6. _____ dreams about catalog cats.

7. _____ feels scared when the catalog arrives.

8. _____ cries after looking at the catalog.

9. _____ has planted a garden before.

10. _____ writes a letter requesting catalog cats.

11. _____ most wants to grow a house of flowers.

12. _____ most wants to grow giant corn.

13. _____ helps plant a garden.

_____

_____

14. _____ talks to the seeds after dark.

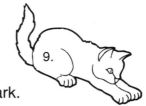

What do you think?

Why didn't Father tell Huey there were no such things as catalog cats? _____

_____

_____

Bonus Box: On the back of this paper, draw and color a garden you would like to grow.

How To Use Page 129

Use this activity after "Our Garden" has been read.

Answer Key

1. Father, Huey, Julian
2. Father, Julian
3. Father
4. Julian
5. Huey
6. Huey
7. Julian
8. Huey
9. Father
10. Huey
11. Huey
12. Julian
13. Father, Huey, Julian
14. Julian

What do you think?

Accept all reasonable answers.

Name_____

Flying High!

Read the cause sentence on each kite tail.
Cut out and glue an effect sentence to each kite tail.

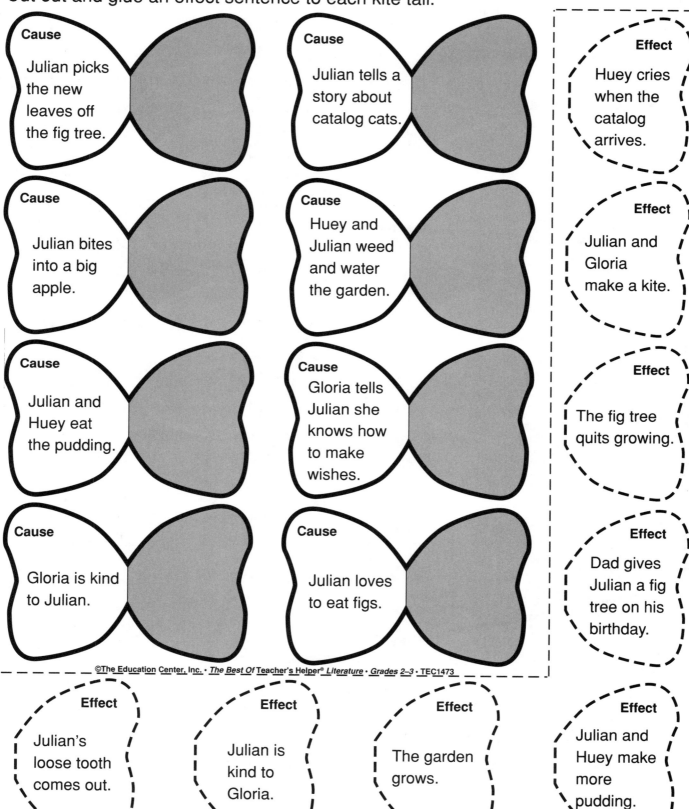

Cause

Julian picks the new leaves off the fig tree.

Cause

Julian tells a story about catalog cats.

Cause

Julian bites into a big apple.

Cause

Huey and Julian weed and water the garden.

Cause

Julian and Huey eat the pudding.

Cause

Gloria tells Julian she knows how to make wishes.

Cause

Gloria is kind to Julian.

Cause

Julian loves to eat figs.

Effect

Huey cries when the catalog arrives.

Effect

Julian and Gloria make a kite.

Effect

The fig tree quits growing.

Effect

Dad gives Julian a fig tree on his birthday.

Effect

Julian's loose tooth comes out.

Effect

Julian is kind to Gloria.

Effect

The garden grows.

Effect

Julian and Huey make more pudding.

How To Use Page 131

Use this activity after the entire book has been read.

Materials Needed For Each Student

— a construction-paper copy of page 131
— a construction-paper copy of the kite pattern below
— four 1/2" x 6" blank paper strips
— pencil
— crayons or markers
— scissors
— glue
— one-foot length of yarn or string
— access to a hole puncher

Directions For The Student

1. Complete the activity on page 131.
2. Cut out the eight kite tails you created and set them aside.
3. Write a wish on each paper strip.
4. Cut out the kite pattern. Personalize both sides of the resulting cutout and hole-punch the cutout where indicated.
5. Thread and tie one end of the yarn length to the bottom of the kite. This is your kite string.
6. At equal intervals along the kite string, glue the blank side of each of four kite tails to the kite string.
7. Glue one wish (paper strip) to the blank side of each glued kite tail.
8. Glue the four remaining kite tails atop the glued kite tails so that the programming is to the outside. A wish and a portion of kite string will be sandwiched between each pair of kite tails. (Demonstrate this step and provide assistance as needed. Remind students that Gloria and Julian attached their wishes to their kite in a similar fashion!)

Kite Pattern

Assembled Project

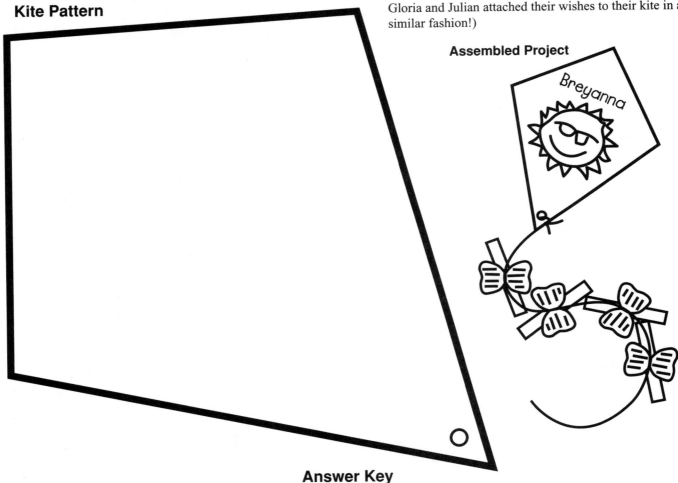

Answer Key

Cause	Effect
Julian picks the new leaves off the fig tree.	The fig tree quits growing.
Julian bites into a big apple.	Julian's loose tooth comes out.
Julian and Huey eat the pudding.	Julian and Huey make more pudding.
Gloria is kind to Julian.	Julian is kind to Gloria.
Julian tells a story about catalog cats.	Huey cries when the catalog arrives.
Huey and Julian weed and water the garden.	The garden grows.
Gloria tells Julian she knows how to make wishes.	Julian and Gloria make a kite.
Julian loves to eat figs.	Dad gives Julian a fig tree on his birthday.

A Message In The Web

Charlotte has written a message in her web for you.
To find the message, read each question.
If the answer is **yes**, color the block **green**.
If the answer is **no**, color the block **yellow**.

Can a <u>message</u> be in a note?	Is a <u>runt</u> huge?	If you have a pretend friend, do you have a good <u>imagination</u>?	Does your mom use <u>spinnerets</u> to knit?	Will a true friend keep a <u>promise</u>?
Could you find an <u>advertisement</u> in a newspaper?	Do you hang wash on a <u>dragline</u>?	Is a <u>gander</u> a male goose?	Is a baby pig called a <u>gosling</u>?	Is a <u>miracle</u> special?
Are true friends <u>devoted</u> to each other?	Can a doctor <u>advise</u> you?	Can a <u>judge</u> give a <u>medal</u> to the winner of a race?	If you are angry, do you look <u>radiant</u>?	Could a <u>photographer</u> take your picture?
Is a <u>crate</u> a wooden box?	Do people eat food from a <u>trough</u>?	Does a pig's face have a <u>snout</u>?	Do you eat with a <u>pitchfork</u>?	Does a <u>balloonist</u> travel by balloon?
Do bragging and <u>boasting</u> mean the same thing?	Do you frown when you <u>chuckle</u>?	Would you serve <u>slops</u> to a pig?	Does a <u>humble</u> person brag?	Does a spider lay eggs in a <u>sac</u>?

Bonus Box: Chapter V has many facts about spiders. Read this part again with a friend. Write three sentences about spiders on the back of this sheet.

Extension Activities

Provide enrichment activities using the Wilbur pattern on page 136 and the following programming suggestions:

— Program the patterns with:
  — vocabulary words for the students to practice in pairs. (See page 133 for vocabulary words.)
  — vocabulary words and definitions; then cut in half as shown. Have students match words and definitions.
— Duplicate the pattern onto white construction paper for each student. Have students color the ears and snouts pink. Then cut the patterns in half and glue 4 1/2-inch strips of writing paper to each half as shown. Have students use the Wilbur writing shapes in the following ways:
  — to write book reports.
  — to write a letter to one of the story characters.
  — to write descriptions of Wilbur. Display student writings on a bulletin board titled "Wonderful Wilbur."
  — to write advertisements for *Charlotte's Web*. Display the students' work in the hall to entice other students to read the book.
— Enlarge the pattern onto white poster board. Color the ears and snout pink; then program with words from the story. Display in a creative-writing center with writing paper and pencils. Story possibilities might include new story endings or Wilbur's further adventures with Charlotte's children.
— Create fun writing paper for student stories by drawing lines onto the pattern before duplicating.
— Program with critical thinking questions (see above for a list of questions) for students to answer independently on writing paper. Or have students discuss questions in pairs.

Critical Thinking Questions

1. Why do you think Charlotte helped Wilbur?
2. What might have happened to Wilbur if he hadn't met Charlotte?
3. What do you think was the most important lesson that Wilbur learned from Charlotte? Why?
4. Do you think Templeton was a good or bad rat? Why?
5. If you could be one character from the story, which character would you most like to be? Why? Which character would you least like to be? Why?

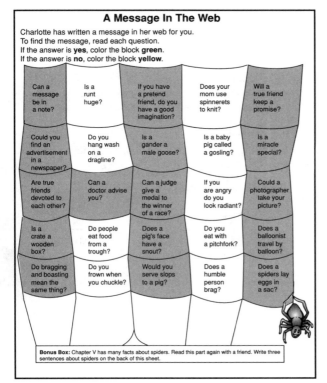

A Message In The Web

Charlotte has written a message in her web for you.
To find the message, read each question.
If the answer is **yes**, color the block **green**.
If the answer is **no**, color the block **yellow**.

Can a message be in a note?	Is a runt huge?	If you have a pretend friend, do you have a good imagination?	Does your mom use spinnerets to knit?	Will a true friend keep a promise?
Could you find an advertisement in a newspaper?	Do you hang wash on a dragline?	Is a gander a male goose?	Is a baby pig called a gosling?	Is a miracle special?
Are true friends devoted to each other?	Can a doctor advise you?	Can a judge give a medal to the winner of a race?	If you are angry do you look radiant?	Could a photographer take your picture?
Is a crate a wooden box?	Do people eat food from a trough?	Does a pig's face have a snout?	Do you eat with a pitchfork?	Does a balloonist travel by balloon?
Do bragging and boasting mean the same thing?	Do you frown when you chuckle?	Would you serve slops to a pig?	Does a humble person brag?	Does a spiders lay eggs in a sac?

Bonus Box: Chapter V has many facts about spiders. Read this part again with a friend. Write three sentences about spiders on the back of this sheet.

Name _____

Some Story!

Read each sentence.
If the sentence is true, circle the letter under true.
If the sentence is false, circle the letter under false.

		True	**False**
1.	Charlotte was a black widow spider.	E	O
2.	Fern fed Wilbur milk in a bottle.	A	I
3.	Mrs. Arable gave Wilbur a bubble bath before they went to the fair.	N	C
4.	Charlotte had seven babies.	R	C
5.	Wilbur made a promise to Templeton before he saved Charlotte's egg sac.	E	Y
6.	When Avery tried to hit Charlotte with a stick, he fell and broke a rotten egg.	V	W
7.	Wilbur won a blue ribbon at the fair.	M	L
8.	Charlotte wrote "Zuckerman's Famous Pig" in her web.	S	T
9.	Fern could hear the animals talk.	H	K
10.	Uncle Homer told Mrs. Arable not to worry about Fern's stories that the animals could talk.	G	T
11.	Templeton was kind and caring toward Wilbur.	J	R
12.	Charlotte died in Uncle Homer's barn.	E	I
13.	Charlotte was Wilbur's best friend.	A	F
14.	All of Charlotte's children left the barn.	B	C

Who is the devoted arachnid in this book?

To find the answer, write the corresponding circled letter from each sentence above on the numbered blanks below.

__ __ A __ __ __ T __ __   A.   __ A __ __ __ __ __ __ __
14 9   11 7 1   10 5   4   6 2 8 12 3 13

Bonus Box: On the back of this sheet, draw and color a Best Friend award for Wilbur to give to Charlotte.

Pattern

See extension activities on page 134 for ways to use this pattern.

©The Education Center, Inc.

Answer Key

	True	False
1.	E	Ⓞ
2.	Ⓐ	Ⓘ
3.	N	Ⓒ
4.	Ⓡ	Ⓒ
5.	Ⓔ	Y
6.	Ⓥ	W
7.	M	Ⓛ
8.	S	Ⓣ
9.	Ⓗ	Ⓚ
10.	G	Ⓣ
11.	J	Ⓡ
12.	E	Ⓘ
13.	Ⓐ	Ⓕ
14.	B	Ⓒ

<u>C H A R L O T T E</u> A. <u>C A V A T I C A</u>

Name _____

A Trio Of Friends

Read each sentence.
Draw a picture to show what happened in the story.
Write a sentence telling what the character is thinking or saying.

Fern loves animals.

Wilbur is devoted to Charlotte.

Charlotte is loyal to Wilbur.

Fern feels proud of Wilbur.

Wilbur feels lonely.

Charlotte shows courage.

Bonus Box: Cut the booklet pages apart on the dotted lines. Make a cover for your booklet. Staple the pages and cover together. Share your booklet with a friend.

Award

Duplicate the buttonhole award on colorful construction paper for each student. Laminate for durability if desired. Using an X-acto® knife, cut along the X in the middle of each award. Present the buttonhole award to each student upon completion of the *Charlotte's Web* unit.

Charlotte's Web is

SOME STORY

Let me tell you about it!

Charlotte's Web is

SOME STORY

Let me tell you about it!

Boxcar Characters

Cut and glue each character above the correct action.

1.

got sick

2.

gave Henry a job

3.

cut Watch's hair

4.

cooked a stew

5.

won the race

6.

gave vegetables to Henry

7.

growled at a noise in the night

Bonus Box: Choose your favorite character from the story. On the back of this sheet, write about why you like this character best.

8.

moved the boxcar to his backyard

©The Education Center, Inc. • *The Best Of* Teacher's Helper® *Literature* • *Grades 2–3* • TEC1473

Mrs. Moore

Dr. Moore

Henry

Jessie

Grandfather

Watch

Violet

Benny

How To Use Pages 139, 141, 143, And 145

Read the story *The Boxcar Children* (Book #1 in The Boxcar Children series) by Gertrude Chandler Warner to your students. Discuss the events and the characters with your students as you read. Engage your children in the extension activity below. Then duplicate copies of pages 139, 141, 143, and 145 for your children.

Extension Activity
Characters And Events

Help your children keep track of the characters and their actions with this chapter-by-chapter activity. Attach a length of bulletin-board paper to your chalkboard. Using a marker, divide the paper into ten equal sections (one section for each character in the story). After reading each chapter of the story, have students dictate the names of any new characters introduced in the story. Write each character's name in a different section of the paper. Then have students dictate the actions of the characters in the chapter. Write the actions below the names of the corresponding characters. (See the examples below.) Periodically review the past events of the story with your children.

Jessie	Benny	Henry	Violet	Baker's wife	Baker	Watch	Dr. Moore	Mrs. Moore	Grand-father
Bandaged Watch's paw	Fell asleep in the bakery	Bought food for the children	Fell asleep in the bakery	Tried to find the children	Tried to find the children	Cried because he was hurt	Gave Henry a job	Showed Henry how to work in the garden	Moved the boxcar to his back-yard

Answer Key

1. Violet got sick.
2. Dr. Moore gave Henry a job.
3. Benny cut Watch's hair.
4. Jessie cooked a stew.
5. Henry won the race.
6. Mrs. Moore gave vegetables to Henry.
7. Watch growled at a noise in the night.
8. Grandfather moved the boxcar to his backyard.

Mixed-Up Meanings

The sentences below are <u>not</u> true.
Change each underlined word to a word that will make the sentence true.
Use a word from the Word Bank. Write the correct sentence on the line.

1. The children ran away because they thought their grandfather was <u>poor</u>.

   _____

   _____

2. The children asked to spend the night in a <u>library</u>. _____

   _____

3. The children made their home in a <u>greenhouse</u>. _____

   _____

4. The children found dishes in a <u>stream</u>. _____

   _____

5. Benny helped Jessie build a <u>doghouse</u>. _____

   _____

6. A stray <u>cat</u> became their pet. _____

   _____

7. The children helped Dr. Moore pick <u>cucumbers</u>. _____

   _____

8. Henry met his grandfather at a <u>picnic</u>. _____

   _____

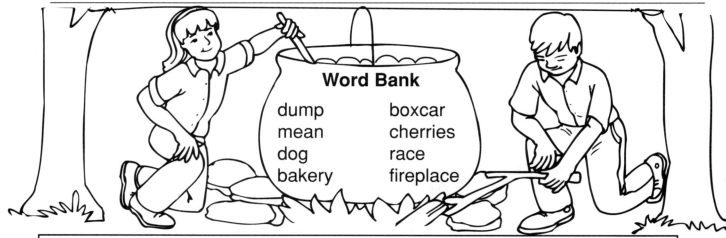

Word Bank

dump	boxcar
mean	cherries
dog	race
bakery	fireplace

Bonus Box: On the back of this sheet, draw a picture of your own grandfather. Write some things you like best about him.

Answer Key

1. The children ran away because they thought their grandfather was <u>mean</u>.
2. The children asked to spend the night in a <u>bakery</u>.
3. The children made their home in a <u>boxcar</u>.
4. The children found dishes in a <u>dump</u>.
5. Benny helped Jessie build a <u>fireplace</u>.
6. A stray <u>dog</u> became their pet.
7. The children helped Dr. Moore pick <u>cherries</u>.
8. Henry met his grandfather at a <u>race</u>.

All Aboard!

by _____

How To Use Page 143

This creative-writing/critical-thinking project makes a great thematic bulletin-board display.

1. Duplicate a copy of page 143 on construction paper for each of your students. Also duplicate a copy of the reproducible writing page below for each child.
2. Have each child color the boxcar as desired. Then have the child write his name on the line provided.
3. Next have the child cut out the boxcar on the outer bold lines.
4. Have the child cut on the dotted lines and fold back on the bold lines so that the flaps fold open (see the illustration).
5. On the writing page, have the child write about one of the topics listed.
6. Have him cut out the writing page on the outer bold line. Then have the child squeeze a trail of glue along its outer edges.
7. Have the child position the boxcar cutout atop the writing page, aligning the borders with the inside of the window cutout.
8. Display children's projects side by side on a railroad-track display.

Writing Topics

— Imagine that you have joined the Boxcar Children. Write part of the story with you in it.

— Write how the story would have changed if the children had lived in one of the following shelters:
  — a cave
  — a houseboat
  — a spaceship
  — a tree house

— Write how the story would have been different if Henry had gone to work for another kind of person such as a little old lady, a mad scientist, or an alien in disguise.

Reproducible Writing Page

Name _____

Just Suppose

Read each question.
Write how the story might have changed.

1. What do you think would have happened if the children had not found the old boxcar? _____

_____

_____

2. What do you think would have happened if Henry had not found a job with Dr. Moore? _____

_____

_____

3. If Violet had not gotten sick, how would the story have changed? _____

_____

_____

4. What do you think would have happened if Dr. Moore had not known about the children's grandfather? _____

_____

Bonus Box: On the back of this sheet, draw a picture of your favorite part of the story. Below the picture, write about what you drew.

Answer Key

Answers will vary.

Learning About Lucas

Cut out the sentences below.
Find eight sentences that tell
  about the story.
Glue the sentences in order.

1.

2.

3.

4.

5.

6.

7.

8.

Bonus Box: Do you think it will be easy for
Lucas to control his obstreperous behavior?
Explain your answer on the back of this paper.

Mrs. Cott finds the word *obstreperous* in the dictionary.	Lucas gets new eyeglasses.
The school nurse scolds Lucas.	Mrs. Hockaday sends Lucas to the school nurse.
Mrs. Hockaday writes a note to Lucas's mother.	Lucas hides the note from Mrs. Hockaday.
Lucas digs his initials into his desk.	Mrs. Cott tells Lucas to turn over a new leaf.
Cricket helps Lucas read the note from Mrs. Hockaday.	Lucas decides eyeglasses will make him a better student.

Note To The Teacher: Use this activity after chapter 2 is read.

How To Use This Literature Unit (Pages 147-154)

The student activities on pages 147, 149, 151, and 153 are designed to accompany Class Clown, a beginning chapter book by Johanna Hurwitz. The book may be read aloud to students, or it may be read by students at a 3.0 or higher reading level. If desired, use a prereading activity to introduce the book (see "Setting The Scene").

Story Summary
Class Clown
By Johanna Hurwitz

It's not easy being the class clown—just ask Lucas Cott. Trouble follows him everywhere! So much trouble, in fact, that Lucas decides to change his ways and become the perfect third grader. Unfortunately Lucas quickly discovers that turning over a new leaf isn't nearly as simple as it seems. Realistic dialogue and everyday situations that sparkle with humor combine to make this beginning chapter book an absolute winner!

Background For The Teacher
Johanna Hurwitz: 1937—

As a nine-year-old child, Johanna Hurwitz had two ambitions in life: to become a librarian and to write books. Today she has fulfilled both of these desires—but it wasn't easy. Hurwitz began working for the New York Public Library while still a high school student. By 1959 she had become a full-fledged librarian, but it wasn't until 1976 that her first book for children was published. Understandably, finding time to write while raising two children was a challenge. In addition, Hurwitz admits that being a children's librarian might have inhibited her early writing efforts. After all, what could she possibly have to say that hadn't already been written in a book somewhere? Eventually Hurwitz got an idea for a short story that was so strong she didn't even stop to wonder if anyone had written it before. That tiny story grew and became the books about Nora (such as *Busybody Nora* and *Nora And Mrs. Mind-Your-Own-Business*). Hurwitz has since found her niche in publishing. To date she has authored more than 30 books for young people.

Setting The Scene

Ask students to think about events that can contribute to a bad day at school (for example: forgetting a homework assignment, spilling a bottle of glue, or having a disagreement with a friend). Be sure to share events that can create a bad day for teachers, too. Then have each youngster write and illustrate a story about the worst school day that he can remember. Encourage students to share their completed projects, or display the projects on a bulletin board titled "It Just Wasn't My Day!" Follow up this activity by reading aloud or asking stu-dents to read the first chapter in the book. In this chapter, "A Note From Mrs. Hockaday," Lucas Cott has a very bad day!

Answer Key

1. Lucas digs his initials into his desk.
2. Mrs. Hockaday writes a note to Lucas's mother.
3. Cricket helps Lucas read the note from Mrs. Hockaday.
4. Mrs. Cott finds the word *obstreperous* in the dictionary.
5. Mrs. Cott tells Lucas to turn over a new leaf.
6. Lucas decides eyeglasses will make him a better student.
7. Mrs. Hockaday sends Lucas to the school nurse.
8. The school nurse scolds Lucas.

Turning Over A New Leaf

Color the leaves. Use the color code.
Explain each answer on the lines.

Color Code
yellow = I agree.
red = I disagree.

Turning over a new leaf
will be easy for Lucas.

_____
_____
_____
_____

It was wrong of Lucas to
bring so many leaves to
school.

_____
_____
_____
_____

Lucas really wants to change his
obstreperous behavior.

_____
_____
_____

Lucas won the bet
with Cricket.

_____
_____
_____
_____
_____

Cricket and Lucas
are both smart.

_____
_____
_____
_____
_____

Mrs. Hockaday is a mean teacher.

_____
_____
_____

Note To The Teacher: Use this activity after chapter 2 is read.

Critical-Thinking/Journal-Writing Questions

Have your students respond orally or in writing to the following thought-provoking questions:

- How do you think your teacher would describe your behavior? How would you describe your behavior? (Chapter 1)
- If you told your teacher or a family member that you were going to turn over a new leaf, how would you be planning to change? (Chapter 2)
- Lucas doesn't think that his behavior was obstreperous on the day he brought a wagon full of leaves to school. Do you agree? Explain your answer. (Chapter 3)
- What do you think was the most important thing that Lucas learned from his bet with Cricket? (Chapter 4)
- Think of something that you do not like to do. How could you make this task more enjoyable? (Chapter 5)
- Do you think Mrs. Hockaday did the right thing when she changed her mind about Lucas's homework assignment? Explain your answer. (Chapter 6)
- What do you think would be the best (worst) thing about performing in a class program such as the Third-Grade Minicircus? (Chapter 7)
- Why do you think Lucas's feelings for Cricket changed? (Chapter 8)

Answer Key

Answers will vary.

Name _____

Colorful Characters

Read the phrases.
Color the shapes to show who you
  think they describe.
You may color more than one shape
  for each phrase.

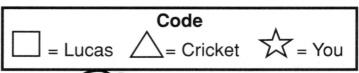

Code

□ = Lucas   △ = Cricket   ☆ = You

□ △ ☆   is helpful

□ △ ☆   likes to tattle

□ △ ☆   likes attention

□ △ ☆   is often forgetful

□ △ ☆   acts very smart

□ △ ☆   likes to make people laugh

□ △ ☆   is sometimes naughty

□ △ ☆   is a good listener

□ △ ☆   follows directions

□ △ ☆   likes to crack jokes

□ △ ☆   wants to be liked

□ △ ☆   has decided on a career

□ △ ☆   has good ideas

□ △ ☆   is smart

□ △ ☆   likes to try new things

□ △ ☆   is well liked

Note To The Teacher: Use this activity after chapter 2 is read.

Answer Key

Answers will vary.

All Funny Business Aside

Describe how you think each character feels.

Julio
when Lucas refuses to talk to him.

Mrs. Cott
as she's sitting in the barbershop.

Mr. Mime
when Lucas gets his head stuck
in the chair.

Arthur
when he finds out he has tonsillitis.

Mr. Cott
when Lucas announces
the minicircus.

Cricket
when she learns Lucas will be in her
fourth-grade classroom.

Mrs. Hockaday
when she hands out the
end-of-the-year awards.

Lucas
as he hurries home on the
last day of school.

©The Education Center, Inc. • *The Best Of* Teacher's Helper® *Literature* • Grades 2–3 • TEC1473

Follow-Up Activity

Lucas Cott's year in third grade brought about many changes in his school work and behavior. Discuss the factors that contributed to these changes. Help youngsters recognize changes they have made during the past school year; then have them identify factors that contributed to these changes. Also invite youngsters to share questions, thoughts, and/or concerns about the next school year. This is a great opportunity to put your students' concerns to rest.

More Books By Johanna Hurwitz

Lucas lives on! To find out more about Lucas's year in fourth grade, read *Teacher's Pet*. In this lighthearted sequel to *Class Clown*, Cricket's expectation of being the teacher's favorite student is dashed by the arrival of a new fourth grader.

Lucas is up to his usual behavior in *School's Out*. In this highly praised book, Lucas delights in getting the best of his new French babysitter, Genevieve, during summer vacation. As the weeks go by, however, Lucas comes to like Genevieve and decides that he must become a better influence on his younger twin brothers.

Answer Key

Answers will vary.

Name _____

A Touch Of Magic

Amber wishes she could change a few things about her life.
In each box, write why Amber would like to change that part of her life.

Her best friend moving away.	Her mom and dad separating.

Jimmy Russell and Bobby Clifford teasing her.

Her dad moving to Paris, France.	Her mom thinking about dating.

Bonus Box: What would you like to change about your life? On the back of this sheet, write one thing you would like to change and why.

How To Use This Literature Unit
(Pages 155–160)

The student activities on pages 155, 157, and 159 are designed to accompany *You Can't Eat Your Chicken Pox, Amber Brown*—a chapter book by Paula Danziger.

Story Summary
You Can't Eat Your Chicken Pox, Amber Brown
By Paula Danziger

Whew! Amber Brown has survived third grade! It's been a tough year—her parents separated and her best friend Justin moved away. But Amber is looking forward to a great summer. In just a few days, she flies to London with her Aunt Pam. After the two tour London, they'll head to Paris, where Amber will see her father for the first time in a very long time.

But even the best-laid plans can unexpectedly go awry. While in London, Amber discovers that her bug bites are not bites at all—they are chicken pox! Instead of a trip to Paris, an itchy Amber is cooped up in a London *flat*. No doubt your students will be itching to find out how Amber Brown copes with this unexpected turn of events.

How To Use Page 155

Use this activity after chapter 2 has been read.

Background For The Teacher
Paula Danziger: 1944–

Paula Danziger loves to write for and about kids. Drawing her inspiration from children she knows or has met, the author writes stories that appeal to young and old alike. And her personal passions—which include a love for life, travel, people, and pinball—make her as interesting as the characters she creates!

Born in Washington, DC, and raised in New York, Danziger knew from second grade on that she wanted to be a writer. She began her career as a teacher, but the success of her first book, *The Cat Ate My Gymsuit*, encouraged Danziger to write full-time. And it has been nonstop for the author ever since! Though she has written and published several books for older readers, her first chapter book for seven- to nine-year-olds was *Amber Brown Is Not A Crayon*—the first book in the Amber Brown series. She has since published *You Can't Eat Your Chicken Pox, Amber Brown* and *Amber Brown Goes Fourth*—the second and third books in the series. Hopefully Danziger has even more escapades in mind for her spunky heroine!

Setting The Scene

Poll your class to discover how many students have had chicken pox. Ask students who have had the virus to tell how and when they discovered they had it. Also find out how this itchy virus affected their immediate plans. For example, did anyone miss a soccer game, a birthday party, or a trip to the zoo because he came down with the chicken pox? Or did anyone miss a dental appointment or a math test? Ask students what might be the best and the worst things about getting chicken pox. If students are familiar with Amber Brown, they may also like to predict how this spunky heroine will cope with a case of the pox!

Amberino Visits London

During her first week in London, Amber has some
good times and some not-so-good times.
Read the events.
Use the code to color the circles.

Color Code
a good time = red
a not-so-good time = blue

○	○	○	○	○
Feeds the pigeons.	Feels bored.	Takes a bus tour.	Is unable to leave the *flat.*	Talks to her dad daily.
○	○	○	○	○
Gets chicken pox.	Takes a lot of pictures.	Finds out she can't go to Paris.	Gets stuck in a *lift.*	Learns that her dad is coming to London.

Color the picture of Amber in the elevator.
Cut on the dotted lines.

The
Ups
And
Downs
Of
London

Up Times

Down Times

157

Materials Needed For Each Student

— copy of page 157
— crayons or markers
— scissors
— 6" x 18" strip of colored construction paper
— glue
— 2-foot length of curling ribbon
— tape

How To Use Page 157

1. Use this activity after chapter 9 has been read.
2. Have each student complete page 157 by following the directions provided.
3. Distribute the colored construction paper, glue, ribbon, and tape.

Directions For Students

1. Refer to the poster Amber is holding in the illustration on page 157; then glue the three labels ("Up Times," "Down Times," and "The Ups And Downs Of London") on your construction paper as shown.
2. Glue the events that were good times (red circles) near the top of the construction paper and the events that were not-so-good times (blue circles) near the bottom of the construction paper. Refer to Amber's poster on page 157 for placement.
3. Cut two small slits as indicated in the elevator cutout. Starting at the front of the cutout, thread one end of the ribbon length through the top slit. Then thread the same ribbon end through the bottom slit. Slide the elevator cutout to the center of the ribbon.
4. Cut two small slits near the opposite ends of the construction paper and thread the ribbon's ends through the slits as shown on Amber's poster. Place the project facedown and pull the ribbon taut; then securely tape the ribbon's ends to the back of the construction paper.
5. Flip the project over. Carefully slide the elevator up and down the ribbon.

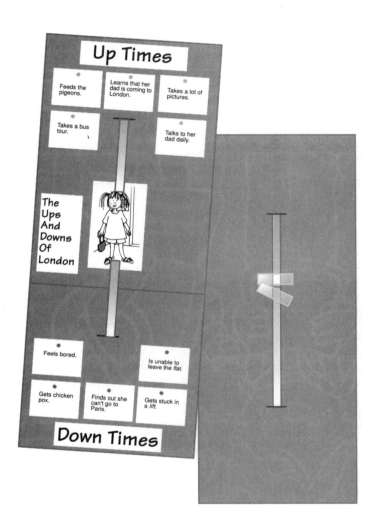

Answer Key
(The order of answers will vary.)

Good Times =
(red circles)

Takes a lot of pictures.
Feeds the pigeons.
Learns that her dad is coming to London.
Takes a bus tour.
Talks to her dad daily.

Not-So-Good Times =
(blue circles)

Gets chicken pox.
Feels bored.
Finds out she can't go to Paris.
Is unable to leave the *flat.*
Gets stuck in a *lift.*

Amber's Scrapbook

Read each caption about Amber's trip.
Draw and color a picture to match.

Feeding the pigeons was the best!	Getting chicken pox was the worst!	The plane trip to London was long.
It was fun riding a double-decker bus around London.	Dr. Kelly came to the *flat*.	Getting stuck in the *lift* was pretty scary.
I was so happy to see my dad!	The Museum Of The Moving Image was very fun.	

Queen Elizabeth II

Cut on the dotted lines.
Stack the pictures in the order that the events
  happened in the story.

Bonus Box: List some or all of the following words on the last page of your scrapbook: *loo, lift, flat, chip, crisp, queue, circus, knickers, Tube, Underground.* Next to each word, write what the word means in London.

Materials Needed For Each Student

— copy of page 159
— crayons or markers
— scissors
— two 4 1/2" x 6" pieces of light-colored construction paper
— five 4 1/2" x 6" pieces of manila paper
— access to a hole puncher
— one-foot length of yarn
— glue

How To Use Page 159

1. Use this activity after the entire book has been read.
2. Have each student complete page 159 by following the directions provided.
3. Distribute the construction paper, manila paper, yarn, and glue.

Directions For Students

1. To make a scrapbook, stack the manila pages between the construction-paper covers. Hole-punch two holes in the left margin of the front cover; then use that cover as a guide to punch holes in each of the remaining paper pieces. Stack and align the project. Thread the yarn through the punched holes; then securely tie the yarn's ends and fashion a bow.
2. Write the title "Amber's Trip To London" on the front cover of the resulting booklet; then decorate the front and back covers to your liking.
3. Glue the picture cutouts from page 159 on the first four scrapbook pages. You may glue two pictures on the front of each page, or you may glue one picture on the front and one picture on the back of each page.
4. Complete the Bonus Box activity on the last scrapbook page.

Book Corner
London

Kidding Around London: A Young Person's Guide To The City • Written by Sarah Lovett & Illustrated by Michael Taylor • Distributed by Wright Group Publishing, Inc.; 1989

The Inside-Outside Book Of London • Written & Illustrated by Roxie Munro • Dutton Children's Books, 1996

Pop-Up London • Written & Illustrated by Anne Wild • Parkwest Publications, Inc.; 1985

Answer Key

The plane trip to London was long.
It was fun riding a double-decker bus around London.
Feeding the pigeons was the best!
Getting chicken pox was the worst!
Dr. Kelly came to the *flat*.
Getting stuck in the *lift* was pretty scary.
The Museum Of The Moving Image was very fun.
I was so happy to see my dad!

Bonus Box Answers: *loo* = bathroom, *lift* = elevator, *flat* = apartment, *chip* = French fry, *crisp* = potato chip, *queue* = waiting line, *circus* = circle, *knickers* = underpants, *Tube* = subway in London, *Underground* = subway in London